MAKE YOUR CHOICE

Speeches for the younger Actress

Edited by

JACQUELINE STOKER

L.R.A.M., R.A.M./Dip.

with a Preface by

MARJORIE LYON

F.T.C.L., L.R.A.M.

SAMUEL   FRENCH

LONDON

NEW YORK   TORONTO   SYDNEY   HOLLYWOOD

© 1975 by Samuel French Ltd

MADE AND PRINTED IN GREAT BRITAIN BY
LATIMER TREND & COMPANY LTD PLYMOUTH

MADE IN ENGLAND

To Barbara Bunch

CONTENTS

AUTHOR INDEX

ACKNOWLEDGEMENTS

For permission to print or reprint copyright extracts from copyright works in this volume the compiler and publishers are grateful to the following authors, translators, their representatives and publishers:

Louisa Alcott: (from *Little Women*, George Philip & Son Ltd) the Publishers, and the adaptor George Holroyd

Jean Anouilh: (from *The Lark*, Samuel French Ltd) the Publishers and the translator Christopher Fry

John Arden and Margaretta D'Arcy: (from *The Business of Good Government*, Methuen & Co. Ltd) the Authors

Jane Austen: (from *Pride and Prejudice*, Samuel French Ltd) the Publishers

J. M. Barrie: (from *Dear Brutus*, Samuel French Ltd) the Publishers

Rudolf Besier: (from *The Barrets of Wimpole Street*, Gollancz) the Author and Samuel French Ltd

Bertolt Brecht: (from *The Good Person of Szechwan*, Methuen & Co. Ltd) the Author and The International Copyright Bureau

Lewis Carroll: (from *Alice Through the Looking Glass*, Samuel French Ltd) the Publishers

Colette and Anita Loos: (from *Gigi*, Samuel French Ltd) the Publishers

Reginald Denham and Mary Orr: (from *Minor Murder*, Samuel French Ltd) the Publishers

Frances Goodrich and Albert Hackett: (from *The Diary of Anne Frank*, Samuel French Ltd) the Publishers

Nicholas Stuart Gray: (from *Beauty and the Beast* and *The Tinder Box*, Oxford University Press) the Author and the Publishers

Grimm: (from *Snow White and the Seven Dwarfs*, Samuel French Ltd) the adaptor Jesse Braham White

David Halliwell: (from *A Last Belch For the Great Auk*, unpublished) the Author and Spokesmen

Thomas Hardy: (from *A Day At The Fair*, based on the short story *On the Western Circuit*, Samuel French Ltd) the adaptor Frank Harvey

W. H. Hudson: (from *Green Mansions*, Gerald Duckworth & Co. Ltd) the Publishers

Henrik Ibsen: (from *The Wild Duck*, Penguin Books Ltd) the translator, Una Ellis-Fermor and the Publishers

Philip Johnson: (from *Charade*, Samuel French Ltd) the Author

A. W. Lintern: (from *The Goose Girl*, Pitman Publishing Co) the Author and the Publishers

Violet Methley: (from *Freckles*, Samuel French Ltd) the Author

A. A. Milne: (from *Toad of Toad Hall*, Samuel French Ltd) the Author

T. B. Morris: (from *Future Mother of the Race*, Samuel French Ltd) the Author

James Reeves: (from *The King Who Took Sunshine*, Heinemann Educational Books) the Author and the Publishers

Arnold Ridley: (from *Easy Money*, Samuel French Ltd) the Author

André Roussin: (from *Figure of Fun*, Samuel French Ltd) the Author and the adaptor Arthur Macré

Jean-Paul Sartre: (from *The Flies*, Hamish Hamilton) from *Two Plays* by J.-P. Sartre. Copyright Editions Gallimard. Translated by Stuart Gilbert, copyright 1946 Hamish Hamilton

Peter Shaffer: (from *Five Finger Exercise*, Samuel French Ltd) the Author

George Bernard Shaw: (from *Pygmalion*, Penguin Books Ltd) The Society of Authors on behalf of the Bernard Shaw Estate

R. B. Sheridan: (from *The Rivals*, Samuel French Ltd) the Publishers

Dodie Smith: (from *Call It A Day* and *I Capture the Castle*, Samuel French Ltd) the Publishers

Hugh Stewart: (from *A Room In the Tower*, Samuel French Ltd) the Author

Tom Stoppard: (from *Enter A Free Man*, Faber & Faber Ltd) the Author

John Van Druten: (from *I Am A Camera*, Evans Brothers Ltd) the Author and Curtis Brown Ltd

Kate Douglas Wiggins: (from *Rebecca of Sunnybrook Farm*, A. & C. Black Ltd), the Author and the Publishers

Harcourt Williams: (from *Goldylocks and the Three Bears*, Samuel French Ltd) the Author

Christa Winslow: (from *Children in Uniform*, Samuel French Ltd) the Author

PREFACE

As an adjudicator, examiner, and teacher I am very grateful to Jacqueline Stoker for her book of Speeches for the Younger Actress.

It is an interesting and imaginative selection, and not only covers a wide age group, but does not keep to the few selections so often presented.

It will be invaluable to teachers who do not always have easy access to a large drama library. I hope the student will try to own their personal copy. (Then we shall not have *our* personal libraries depleted, bless them!) Also it is so good for them to read selections other than the one they are performing.

I wish Jacqueline Stoker every success which this book should bring her.

MARJORIE LYON

INTRODUCTION

The solo drama selections included here are intended for the younger actress—six to sixteen plus—to be performed at auditions, festivals, examinations, etc.; in fact wherever *Own Choice* appears in a syllabus.

Ideas for this book first came to me whilst attending various Music, Speech and Dance festivals in and around London where the choice of material for the Drama and Duologue sections was left entirely to the discretion of the speech and drama teacher. In most cases, the choice in the classes was noticeably limited. To take one example—eight contestants performed *Antigone* in a class of fourteen!

I believe it to be essential and indeed most advisable for the teacher to keep abreast of present-day trends in modern drama, and not to rely year-after-year upon satisfactory yet well-worn material.

Therefore I hope that the following progressive selections will be both of assistance to the teacher and a new and stimulating experience for the young actress.

JACQUELINE STOKER

GOLDYLOCKS AND THE THREE BEARS

GOLDYLOCKS

Goldylocks is walking through the forest, when she notices a little house

What a dear little house! I have often wanted to see inside it. (*Putting her head in through the window, and looking round*) I wonder if the door is open? (*She tries the door, finds it open and goes in*) I wonder who lives here. (*Looking about*) I wish I could find my mittens. I left them in the garden last night. (*She sees porridge on the table*)—Oh!—Porridge! Doesn't it smell good! I'm very hungry. I suppose I mustn't taste—well just a drip, about so big. (*Sees a big bowl*) I will take it out of this big bowl—ugh!—that's too hot. What about this. (*Tries middle bowl*) No, that's too cold. (*Tries little bowl*) It's lovely—I must have a wee bit more, just another half spoonful. Oh, it is so good. There! I've eaten it all up. Now I think I will have a little rest before I start home. This fine big handsome chair will do. (*Tries it*) Oh! It is too hard. Perhaps this one will be more comfortable. (*Tries it*) No. It's much too soft. Look at that weeny-teeny little one. I'm sure that will be just right—(*tries it*)—and so it is! It's a darling little chair. Oh! Oh! Oh! (*She falls through the bottom*) Oh! I've broken it. What a pity! Well, I must rest somewhere. Suppose I try the bedroom. (*Up stage beds*) This big bed looks inviting. (*She gets in*) Oh dear! This is much too high. I feel as if I were sleeping on a mountain. (*She gets into the next*) How very provoking! This is much too low. Whoever heard of sleeping on the floor? That would never do. I had better see what the little one is like with the crazy coverlet—(*gets in*)—oh, um!—how cosy! It's like my very own bed at home. I *mustn't* really go to sleep, but I might just close my eyes for a while and just pretend, yes, oh (*yawns*). I can't keep awake, oh, goodnight, goodnight. (*Falls asleep*)

HARCOURT WILLIAMS

1

SNOW WHITE AND THE SEVEN DWARFS

SNOW WHITE

Queen Brangomar has commanded Berthold, the Chief Huntsman, to take Snow White into the forest, kill her, and bring back her heart. Berthold takes Snow White to the forest but cannot commit the deed. Snow White is left alone but soon a brown bird flies past and calls for her to follow. They have come a long way and Snow White is tired and hungry, but as she sees the house, where the brown bird was leading her, she runs up to peep in through the window

Oh, was it toward this light you were leading me, brown bird? Why, it's a little house! Are you flying away now? Please let me thank you first. I blow you a kiss! He's gone. Perhaps birds don't like kisses, their faces are so sharp. (*Calling after him*) Good-bye, little friend! (*She looks cautiously through the window into the house*) What a queer little room! Seven beds and all so small. There must be lots of children in the family. Nobody with so many children could be wicked. (*She calls*) May I come in? (*As there is no answer she knocks at the door, then opens it a crack*) Please may I come in to rest just for a moment? I'm lost in the forest. (*Still no answer. She steals into the room and looks about*) Nobody at home. But they couldn't mind if I sat down, just a minute. Oh, there's the children's supper all laid out. I'm so hungry! If I took just a tiny bit from each place, I'm sure they wouldn't mind. (*She goes to the table, and as she nibbles a morsel at each place, she sings to herself*)

> A drink of water from this cup,
> Of porridge just a single sup;
> Of honey just a drop to spread
> Over this bit of crusty bread.
> One corner of this barley-cake,
> One nut—and for dessert I'll take
> A single cherry of these four,
> And not a single mouthful more,
> No, not a single mouthful more!

Now I ought to do something to pay for my supper. There's plenty to be done. It isn't at all a tidy house. (*She yawns; and then, shaking herself*) Wake up, Snow White! You mustn't get sleepy yet; not till the people come home. (*But she cannot stifle another yawn*) There's a broom. Suppose I sweep a little. (*She begins, but the broom raises such a cloud of dust that she has to stop*) Dear me, that only makes things worse. This floor needs a good scrubbing. I might make up the beds. (*She goes to the biggest bed, but she is so tired that she sits down on it a moment before beginning*) This one looks as if it hadn't been made for years and years and years. I wonder if it's as humpy to lie on as it is to sit on. (*She lies down to try*

2

it) Oh, it's more. . . . It's humpy and bumpy . . . and bumpy and humpy . . . and . . . (*Her voice trails away into silence. She has fallen asleep*)

For a time all is quiet in the room. Soon the seven dwarfs return home to find Snow White sleeping on one of their beds. In their excitement they forget to be quiet

Snow White stirs in her sleep; then wakes and sits up

Where is this? Oh, there are the children that live here. Why, they're *not* children. They're queer, little old men. They'll never let me stay with them. (*She rises, and standing by the bed says shyly*) I beg your pardon. (*The Dwarfs turn suddenly. Snow White makes a little curtsey*) I'm sorry if I've disturbed you; but I was lost in the forest, and when I saw your house I was so tired and hungry I came in and took a little food—without asking. Then I'm afraid I fell asleep. (*She waits for an answer, but the Dwarfs gaze at her in silence, so she falters on*) I'd pay for it, but I haven't any money. (*She stops. Again a silence*) So all I can do is to say, "Thank you—and—good night." (*She moves reluctantly to the door. The Dwarfs sigh deeply. She turns for a farewell curtsey*) Thank you *very* much. (*She half shuts the door behind her, then re-opens it to repeat*) Good night! (*There is no answer except another heavy sigh from the Dwarfs. With sudden pity she bursts out*) Oh, you're not dumb, are you?

A Fairy Tale Play based on the story by the Brothers Grimm
JESSE BRAHAM WHITE

BEAUTY AND THE BEAST

BEAUTY

Jane Clement, who is called Beauty, is staying in the Beast's Castle, but she is homesick. Mikey is a mischievous dragon, and the nephew of Mr Hodge, the Wizard, who is responsible for all the magic

(*Beauty is filling the bowl at the feet of Eros with roses. She crosses to the window to pick one, starts to cross to Eros with it, then turns again and looks out of the window into the darkness*) I wish they wouldn't stay out in the dark. I don't know what to do with them. Mikey is quite troublesome enough without any further encouragement. And the Beast gets disturbed so by the moonlight . . . as though he had not enough already to disturb his poor mind. Oh, he shouldn't go out in the night! Ah, well. . . . (*She sighs, and goes to add her rose to the bowlful*) Oh, Eros—I never thought the statue of love could look so aloof. (*She sighs again*) How silent it is here. I wish there wasn't quite so much silence. (*A minor chord of music sounds through the room, and dies quietly away*) Oh! Oh, dear, I cannot become accustomed to this sort of thing. Now, I mustn't hurt their feelings. (*She speaks politely to the air*) Thank you, I should like you to play to me, very much. (*Another chord sweeps across the room, then a quiet and gentle air is heard*) (*Smiles*) It's very pretty, however you do it. (*She crosses to the table and sets out some dishes*) I hope they'll come in to supper. (*She sighs*) I do wonder how Jessamine and Jonquiline, and Papa, are managing. I wonder what they are having for supper now. Not cold venison and wine. Oh dear, I would like rice pudding. And I always hated them so. (*She crosses to sit on window-seat*) Jonquiline and Jessamine . . . and Papa . . . are you thinking about me, sometimes? Have you forgotten me? (*She takes out her handkerchief and dabs her nose*) Now don't be silly. I'm being as bad as the twins. How could they forget me, in one month? (*She blows her nose firmly, and sniffs a little*) Besides, I haven't forgotten them, so why should they forget me? Don't be silly. You're grown-up now. But oh, Papa . . . Jonquiline . . . Jessamine . . . I do miss you. It's so lonely here, with no-one to talk to, and no-one to hug. (*Out comes her handkerchief again*) And oh, are you remembering about the canary? (*She sits sobbing helplessly and after a moment the door opens*)

NICHOLAS STUART GRAY

4

ALICE THROUGH THE LOOKING-GLASS

ALICE

Alice is playing chess with her big sister

(*Handling the pieces*) That is the Red Queen and that is the White Queen. Oh, yes, and that's the Red King, but he's fallen down, so I think he must be asleep. Oh, and here's the White King. Isn't it funny I can pick up a King in my hand! What would he think if he knew. There, we'll put him next to the White Queen. She looks as if a little kindness and putting her hair in papers would do wonders for her. Oh, Sister, I should love to be a queen. (*Looking at the mirror*) Suppose the glass got all soft like gauze, so that I could step through. It might turn into a sort of mist. Oh, Sister wouldn't it be lovely if I could get into Looking-glass Land and be a queen! There'd be the Red Queen and the White Queen and me. (*She hears a sound*) Oh, Sister, will you, please, put the chess-men away. I think I hear the black kitten crying to come in. (*She runs and fetches the black kitten and stands by her sister*) Oh, Kitty, how naughty you are! You want such a lot of waiting on, you little mischievous darling! Now, don't interrupt me. I'm going to tell you all your faults. One, you squeaked twice when Dinah was washing your face this morning. Now, you can't deny it, Kitty, I heard you. What's that you say? Her paw went into your eye? Well, that's your fault for keeping your eyes open. Fault two, you pulled the white kitten away by the tail just as I had put down a saucer of milk before her. What, you were thirsty, were you? How do you know she wasn't thirsty too? Fault three, you unwound every bit of my wool when I wasn't looking. (*Alice, who has been leaning against her sister, stands up and walks slowly down stage carrying kitten*) That's three faults, Kitty, and you haven't been punished for any of them yet. (*She sits on the floor*) You know, I'm saving up all your punishments for Wednesday week. And if you're not good then, I shall put you right through the looking-glass into Looking-glass House. How would you like that? Do you know, I believe, if you folded your arms and sat up you'd look just like the Red Queen, Kitty. Now do try, there's a dear. If I put you through the looking-glass and you were the Red Queen—(*she is getting sleepy*)—the Red Queen in the looking-glass, and the White Queen, and the White Knight ... (*She falls asleep*)

LEWIS CARROLL

Dramatized by V. A. PEARN

5

THE KING WHO TOOK SUNSHINE

JOANNA

Joanna is the daughter of the King and Queen of Portamento. This country is badly in need of money and the King wants her to marry a wealthy Duke; but Joanna is secretly in love with Godolphin, the kitchen-boy

(*Joanna is carrying a pair of slippers*) Good-evening, Father. (*Kissing him*) Have you had a very tiring day? Here, sit down and let me put them on. . . . That's right. Oh, I'll be careful of your chilblains. Is that more comfortable? Father, I have been thinking about a suitable husband, but I have come to the conclusion that I'm much too young to marry; in fact I don't mean to get married for years and years. What's that? The Duke of Monte Rosa? That sounds nice. What's he like? How old is he? When can I see him? (*The King hands her the portrait, which Joanna and the Queen examine in silent amazement*) You can't mean it. Not that old scarecrow? Father, I . . . I . . . His nose—it's all over the place. His eyes— they don't both look the same way. Father, I don't want to be married at all, and if I did, that odious old circus-freak would be the last man on earth I should choose. I won't marry him—I won't, I won't, I won't! (*She stamps her feet furiously*) Mother, I don't have to marry that man, do I? Oh, do say something, Mother! Surely you can't want to marry your only daughter to *that*! I won't have him, I tell you, I won't.

The King storms out

Joanna throws herself on the settee and sobs angrily. The Queen tries to comfort her

He has no right to marry me to a man I can't stand the sight of. Do go and stop him! Tell him I'll run away! Tell him I'll kill myself! I never will marry that trampled-on sponge-cake, that suet pudding with whiskers, that—oh, it's too bad, it's terrible. Leave me alone, Mother. Go and tell him what I've said.

Queen exits

Joanna buries her head in her hands and sobs quietly

Godolphin enters

I am so unhappy, Godolphin. I am to be married. *There* is the picture of my future husband. Go and have a look at it. (*Godolphin looks at the portrait*) Take a good look at it, and tell me whether you think I can possibly be happy. That's not *my* fancy. It's my father's. The Duke is very rich, and my

6

father needs money. You can never understand what a man will do for money. Oh, Godolphin, what shall I do? Please tell me what to do? (*A pause*) You *do* love me, don't you? Please hold me very tight, and don't let that awful man get hold of me.

JAMES REEVES

SNOW WHITE AND THE SEVEN DWARFS

QUEEN BRANGOMAR

Queen Brangomar is jealous of Snow White's youth and beauty and resolves to have her killed

(*Quite calmly the Queen goes to the bell-cord*) Let me see. I ring three times for the Huntsman. (*She rings*)

Berthold enters

Berthold, I have a task for you. You have been a faithful Chief Huntsman. Suppose I promote you to be Lord High Admiral. As we have no navy, your duties would be light. However, it depends upon your carrying out a task with absolute obedience. Come nearer. The Princess Snow White is to set out for boarding-school this afternoon. You will conduct her. At the Western Gates, you will take the old road that turns to the left.... You will take *that* road. When you have come to the very heart of the forest, then—(*and she hisses the words*)—you will kill the Princess. She has disobeyed me. She must be punished. (*In a terrible voice*) Wait! I know how to make you obey. You have six small children, I believe? Suppose I lock them up in the Great Gray Tower. Think! Can you not hear their voices calling to you from the dark? "We are hungry, Papa!" they will cry, and they will beat on the door with their little hands. At last they will be too weak to cry or beat. Then when all has grown still within the Tower, I will say: "Berthold, here is the key. Go and see how Queen Brangomar punishes disobedience." That's *much* better, Berthold. You understand clearly. Remember the motto, "A task cheerfully done is well done". And, oh, I almost forgot. You must bring me Snow White's heart before midnight, as a proof. Here comes the Prince. Do try to look more pleasant.

JESSE BRAHAM WHITE

TOAD OF TOAD HALL

PHOEBE

Phoebe, the jailer's daughter, enters a dungeon with breakfast on a tray. Toad is sleeping uneasily on a heap of straw in the corner

Good morning, Toad. Slept well? See, I've brought your breakfast. (*Arranging the breakfast*) Nice hot buttered toast and tea. Made it myself, I did. Father said, "Here's the key of number eighty-seven," he said, "and you can take him his breakfast. He's the most notoriousest, dangerous animal in the country," said Father, "and how we shall keep him under lock and key goodness only knows—" His very words. "The most notoriousest, dangerous *and* reckless animal within the four walls of this here castle. And you can take him a couple of old crusts for his breakfast," said Father, "because I must starve and break his indomitable spirit," said Father; "otherwise he'll get the better of me." So I said, "Yes, Father," and as soon as his back was turned I said to myself, "What a shame!" and I made this nice buttered toast. Is that where you live—Toad Hall? Tell me about it. Fancy! And do your friends Mr Badger and Mr Rat and Mr Mole live there with you? You're feeling better, aren't you? (*Looking at him thoughtfully*) Now I wonder. Toad, I feel sorry for you, and I think it's a shame the way you've been treated and I think I see a way in which you might escape. Now listen. I have an aunt who is a washer-woman. Now my aunt does the washing for all the prisoners in the castle. Naturally we keep anything of that sort in the family. She brings the washing back Friday morning—that's today. Now you're very rich—at least you're always telling me so—and for a few pounds I think I could persuade her to lend you her dress and bonnet and so on, and you could escape as the castle washerwoman. You're very much alike in some ways— particularly about the figure. All right, all right. Then you can stop here as a toad. I suppose you want to go off in a coach and four? That's better. (*As she goes out*) With a little trouble you'd make quite a nice toad.

A. A. MILNE

THE TINDER-BOX

PRINCESS GISELLA

The King has made his daughter, the Princess Gisella, a prisoner in the castle to prevent the prophecy of a fortune-teller—that Gisella will marry a common soldier—from coming true. Mommet the Witch has become the Princess's new lady-in-waiting

(In the Princess's room. Gisella sits on a stool by the bed, reading. She looks up and sighs. Then she rubs her hand across her eyes. She rises and goes to the window, with the book in her hands)

How lovely the snow is . . . falling so quietly. I wish I could feel its cold feathers against my cheeks. I wish it could talk to me . . . good evening, snow . . . I've been reading about you in my book. A poem about your white feathers. How odd that I may only read of things, now, and never really know them for myself again. How sad, that I shall stay imprisoned in this tower until I die. But I won't think about that . . . it will make my head ache. I'll read some more about the snow, and not look where it is falling over all the people who are free to enjoy it. *(She runs back to her stool, to read in her book again)*
 . . . know henceforth
 It's the shedding of their feathers
 By the Snow-birds of the North.

The Witch enters, right, through the arch. The Princess starts up with a cry, dropping her book, and backing away

Oh! you always frighten me. None of my other ladies frighten me, like you. *(The Witch pretends to cry, the Princess goes to her with reluctant sympathy)* Please don't cry. I shouldn't have said it, I suppose. Forgive me. My behaviour must seem very strange to you, but remember I have been a prisoner in this tower since I was fifteen . . . for three endless years . . . you'd overlook my stupidity when you think of that, wouldn't you? No, my father will never let me out. He won't. Not ever. Once Father gets an idea into his head, it sticks like a burr. He thinks it would be unkingly to change his mind. Mother can't cope with Father at all. She says she's given up. So here I am, and here I must stay. All because of a fortune-teller and his foolish tongue. I'd rather not talk about it. It makes my head ache. Other girls may dance, and ride, and play . . . but they are not in prison! I can never pick flowers or feed the swans on the lake . . . or stop my horse to speak with children by the road-side! I must only look out of this one window over the roofs of the town, and over the trees, and beyond. And everything that exists . . . in the town, or the forests, or

10

the sea . . . I must read about in books, or forget altogether. And all because my father thinks a king must have everything as he wishes it . . . and because a fortune-teller said I would marry a soldier! A soldier . . . a common, ordinary soldier! I've never met one. Oh, why did you make me speak about it? I shall never sleep tonight. (*She picks up a book and gets into bed*) I shan't sleep tonight, unless I forget my own thoughts in someone else's. Forgive me, if I've been rude to you, Madam Mommet. I'm always nervous with strangers now. I won't read too late. Can't you put a spell on me to make me sleep?

Witch goes out. Gisella reads from her book, sighing

> Sun and stars are free to wander
> Under all eternity . . .
> Who will set me free, I wonder?
> Or must I die?

NICHOLAS STUART GRAY

REBECCA OF SUNNYBROOK FARM

REBECCA

Rebecca is on her way by stage-coach to Riverboro to stay with her two Aunts, Miranda and Jane Sawyer

Good-bye, Mother; don't worry. You know, it isn't as if I hadn't travelled before. (*She is thrown from side to side of the coach*) Mr Cobb, does it cost any more to ride up there with you? It's so slippery and shiny down here, and the stage is so much too big for me, that I rattle round in it till I'm almost black and blue. And the windows are so small I can only see pieces of things, and I've almost broken my neck stretching round to find out whether my trunk has fallen off the back. It's my mother's trunk, and she's very choice of it. (*The coach stops and Rebecca joins Mr Cobb on top*) Oh, this is better! (*The coach moves off again*) This is like travelling! I am a real passenger now, and down there I felt like our setting hen when we shut her up in a coop. I hope we have a long, long ways to go? Only two hours! That will be half-past one; Mother will be at Cousin Ann's, the children at home will have had their dinner, and Hannah cleared all away. I had some lunch, because Mother said it would be a bad beginning to get to the brick house hungry, and have Aunt Mirandy have to get me something to eat the first thing. It's a good growing day, isn't it? Oh dear no, Mr Cobb, I never put my sunshade up when the sun shines. Pink fades awfully you know; and I only carry it to meetin' cloudy Sundays. Sometimes the sun comes out all of a sudden, and I have a dreadful time covering it up. It's the dearest thing in life to me; but it's an awful care. Miss Ross, a lady that paints, gave it to me. Did you notice the pinked double ruffle and white tip and handle. They're ivory. The handle is scarred, you see. That's because Fanny sucked and chewed it in a meetin' when I wasn't looking. I've never felt the same to Fanny since. Yes, Fanny is one of my sisters. There are seven of us in our family. Hannah is the oldest; I come next, then John, then Jenny, then Mark, then Fanny, then Mira. Hannah and I haven't done anything but put babies to bed at night and take them up again in the morning for years and years. But it's finished, that's one comfort; and we'll have a lovely time when we're all grown up. Aunt Miranda wanted Hannah to come to Riverboro instead of me, but Mother couldn't spare her; she takes hold of housework better than I do, Hannah does. I told Mother last night if there was likely to be any more children while I was away I'd have to be sent for, for when there's a baby it always takes Hannah and me both, for Mother has the cooking and the farm. My mother's name is Aurelia Randall. Our names are Hannah Lucy Randall, Rebecca Rowena Randall, John Halifax Randall, Jenny Lind Randall, Marquis Randall, Fanny Ellsler Randall, and Miranda Randall. Mother named half of us and Father the other half; but we didn't come

12

out even, so they both thought it would be nice to name Mira after
Aunt Miranda, in Riverboro. They hoped it might do some good; but
it didn't and now we call her Mira. We are all named after somebody in
particular. Hannah is Hannah at *The Window Binding Shoes*; and I am .
taken out of *Ivanhoe*. John Halifax was a gentleman in a book; Mark
is after his uncle, Marquis de Lafayette, that died a twin. We don't call
him Marquis, only Mark. Jenny is named after a singer, and Fanny for
a beautiful dancer; but Mother says they're both misfits for Jenny can't
carry a tune, and Fanny's kind of stiff-legged. I think that's all there is
to tell about us, Mr Cobb. This is a great trip, and we've got real well
acquainted haven't we?

KATE DOUGLAS WIGGINS

From the novel

THE TINDER-BOX

WITCH

Peter, a simple young soldier, lies asleep on a low bank under a signpost which says "To Kastelburg". He shifts uneasily, wakes, yawns, and shivers. Then he lights a fire, huddles down close to it, and goes to sleep again. The Witch enters, she is small, energetic with bright eyes which peer suspiciously from side to side

Who's been lighting a fire? That's very dangerous! Might set light to the grass. Oh, on the road, eh? No grass. Well, there might have been. Careless! Who's that? (*She crosses to Peter. She lifts a fold of his cloak with her staff, and peers at him*) Dangerous to sleep near a fire! Might set his clothes alight. He hasn't . . . but he could of! Careless thing! Clothes all torn, anyway . . . and his hair! Tt! All anyhow! And what a place to sleep in. Now, I wonder if I'm on the right path? Dangerous to get lost in the dark! Where's my map? (*She produces a small parchment map from a pocket and turns it about and about, peering at it crossly*) Can't see a thing! My eyes are going old on me. But what's the good of being a witch if I can't work a small wonder occasionally? Listen, you moon, up there! Can you hear me? Right! (*She waves her hands in a mystic way*) Ooo . . . ooo . . . ooo . . . ooo . . .
      By the magic of my rune,
      Shine a little brighter, moon
(*The moonlight brightens considerably, and the witch looks pleased with herself*) Good bit of magic, that. Useful for dark nights and dirty deeds! (*She peers at the signpost, and again at the map*) Yes, this looks like the right place. "Signpost pointing to the town" . . . yes, that's it. Ah, wait . . . there's lots of signposts! This might not be the one. Dangerous habit, jumping to conclusions! What else does it say? "A great old hollow tree" . . . and there is a great old hollow tree, sure enough. It's the right place! Clever old witch, oh very clever old witch! I found out about the treasure by magic, and I made the map by magic, and I got here by magic, and it's the right place! Lovely old witch! (*She crosses to look up into the tree*) Pretty tree. Beautiful hollow tree. All nobbled and gnarled, with that great treasure glittering deep under your roots—what's that? A mouse! Horrid thing! Shoo . . . run away! That's right. No business in that tree, of all trees! And there's his disgusting bit of bread . . . soon get rid of that! (*She flicks the bit of bread away, and dusts her fingers*) Now for the treasure! (*She starts to climb the lower branches*) Nasty spiky branches, turn away your rough edges. Don't hinder me . . . ow! (*She slides down again, and glares at the tree*) It bit me! How dare it! How could it? Trees don't bite. Oh, now, if trees start biting that will be dangerous! I do believe it was that mouse! Wicked mouse! Shoo . . .

14

shoo . . . Oh, you won't run away this time? You're going to sit there, are you, and[bite me when I try to climb the tree? Shoo . . . you wretched thing! I suppose you're angry because I threw away your bit of bread? Have it your own way. I shan't go up there to be bitten by a mouse. Mouse-bites can be very dangerous. Especially white-mouse-bites! Angry-white-mouse-bites! I'll get some magic working on this. I'll call my mystical slaves! (*She waves her hands mysteriously*) Ooo . . . ooo . . . ooo . . . ooo . . .

> Moonlight, magic, hollow tree . . .
> Swiftly bring my slaves to me.

(*She taps her foot impatiently after a moment*) Come along, come along! I'm not going to do it again! Always late, those two! I'll have to evaporate them, and get a couple of hard-working demons!

NICHOLAS STUART GRAY

THE KING WHO TOOK SUNSHINE

ROSALBA

Rosalba, former nurse to the Princess Joanna, is helping the Queen to find a cure for the King's bad temper

The Royal Magician is nowhere to be found. Whenever there's trouble, you know he always turns himself into a black beetle or something, and gets out of it like that. Besides, *he* wouldn't be any good, if you ask me. They're all the same, these men magicians. They can do a good showy piece of magic, like raising an army out of marrow-seeds or planting a forest overnight, but when it comes to anything delicate, as you might say, then give me a woman every time. No, no, Ma'am, not a witch; I wouldn't dream of having dealings with the like of *them*. But sometimes an old soul who's not quite so simple as she looks and has studied a bit— you know, herbs and that—that's the sort of person who might help, if anyone could. Well, Your Majesty, I don't suppose you'd know her, but old Meg, the henwife, who lives in a cottage in the wood—they say *she's* very clever—not at all as stupid as she might be. She spends a good deal of time in the kitchen, Ma'am—doing a bit of cooking, boiling up this and that—nobody minds her and she's quite harmless. She absent-mindedly made the cat talk in Latin once, and gave the cook a bit of a fright. But she promised never to do it again. She's got a spell for curing chilblains—very good it is too, nine times out of ten. To cut a long story short, Ma'am, I've been talking to her this very evening—all about the King and his bad temper. I hope it wasn't a liberty. She says she'll do what she can. Will you see her? Oh, I knew you would, Ma'am! I've got her here—just outside. (*Going to door*) Thank you *so* much—very gracious of you, most obliging and gracious, I'm sure. Meg! Come in, Meg.

JAMES REEVES

THE GOOSE-GIRL

AGATHA

Grizelda, the rightful betrothed of Stefan, but now the unfortunate goose-girl, is suffering great humiliation from Agatha, her step-sister, who has assumed her identity

(*Outraged*) Silence! Here, you, sir—what's-your-name—take this fool outside and thrash him. How dare he address me—*me*! (*To Grizelda*) So you are happy, well-clothed and well-fed—we must see to that. We cannot have you too comfortable, my dear, can we? I shall see that you have nothing but a sack to wear, nothing but a cellar to sleep in, and naught but a crust and a cup of water each day. You shall be roused each morning at the earliest hour, and kept at work until dark. How I shall gloat over you! I shall come and see you every day, in your misery, and each time I shall wear a new dress and a new set of jewels. Just you wait until I am married to Stefan—I shall be mistress of the palace, and my word shall be law. (*Agatha looks at her, sneeringly, for some moments, hoping that she will break down and beg for mercy*) So I cannot make you talk— but I can make you writhe. Falada is dead—the grooms took him out and cut off his head. I ordered it. Do you hear? *I ordered it.* And now I am going to write to my *dear* step-father and tell him how happy *we* are. I shall tell him that Grizelda and Stefan are to be married tomorrow. Now, *get out*, you—you goose-girl.

A. W. LINTERN

LITTLE WOMEN

BETH

Elizabeth (Beth) March, has a shy manner, a timid voice, and a peaceful expression which is seldom disturbed; but in this scene Beth is in a very distraught state as the Hummel baby has just died

(*Beth comes in and staggers to a chair, sighing. She is in her outdoor clothes and has been crying*) You've had the scarlet fever, haven't you? Oh, Jo, the baby's dead! (*Sobbing*) Mrs Hummel's baby; it died in my lap before she got home. It wasn't dreadful, Jo, only so sad! I saw in a minute that it was sicker, but Lotty said her mother had gone for a doctor, so I took baby and let Lotty rest. It seemed asleep, but all of a sudden it gave a little cry, and trembled, and then lay very still. I tried to warm its feet, and Lotty gave it some milk, but it didn't stir, and I knew it was dead. I just sat and held it softly till Mrs Hummel came with the doctor. He said it was dead. "Scarlet fever, Ma'am. Ought to have called me before", he said crossly. Mrs Hummel told him she was poor, and had tried to cure baby herself, but now it was too late, and she could only ask him to help the others, and trust to charity for his pay. He smiled then, and was kinder; but it was very sad. He turned round, all of a sudden, and told me to go home and take belladonna right away, or I'd have the fever. Don't be frightened, I guess I shan't have it badly. (*Anxiously*) Don't let Amy come; she never had it and I should hate to give it to her. Can't you and Meg have it over again? Now I'd better go to my room.

LOUISA M. ALCOTT

Adapted from the novel

Edited and dramatized by George H. Holroyd, M.A.

18

FRECKLES—A SKETCH

FRECKLES

Freckles, a school-girl, is tremendously excited and rushes into the school-room where she interrupts Joan and Dora, two friends, who are doing their homework

Listen to me! My Godmother is coming tomorrow. She's coming tomorrow! She's simply lovely, and she dresses most beautifully, and she's frightfully rich, and she's a perfect darling—I've got heaps of photographs of her. (*Losing her excitement, and looking terribly sad and disconsolate, sitting down near the others*) That's the awful part of it—the part that spoils everything. I sent her a photograph of me and it didn't show a single freckle, but when she actually sees me, she's going to have a terrible shock. I'm sure she won't like me—and I *do* so want her to! (*Dejectedly*) They make me look so awful. I don't believe anyone could love a person with freckles. I don't want my Godmother to put up with it, and I mean to help them—so that's why I've bought this. (*Producing a small flat jar*) I saw about it in an advertisement. It's called "Cleopatra Cream". Listen to what it says on the label. (*Reading*) "This cream will remove all spots, pimples, sunburn, freckles, and all other blemishes of the skin. The cream should be smeared thickly on the face or hands, on retiring to bed at night, and one application will often show most marked results." (*Triumphantly*) There! I'm going to try it, and I shall apply it thickly when I go to bed tonight—*very thickly!* I shan't put it on until after Miss Gedge has been round to put the lights out, I can easily do it in the dark. Oh, won't it be splendid if all my freckles have disappeared in the morning, or even if they're much fainter? The bottle wouldn't tell lies, would it? It *must* be true if it says so on the label. (*She gets up and dances round the room, waving the jar over her head, then comes down centre again*) My Godmother is coming for me in her motor-car very early tomorrow morning—before breakfast. She's asked permission to take me out for the whole day! And we're going to a matinee, and into the park, and to do some shopping, and have lunch somewhere with a band, and do all sorts of lovely things! And it would have been quite spoilt if I'd been thinking all the time how she must hate my freckles! So when I bring my Godmother up here, promise me, both of you, that you won't call me Freckles before her—I do hate it so! Remember to say Marjorie! You *mustn't* forget! And now I'm going to hide away this darling little blessing of a pot of cream on the shelf in my cubicle—ready for tonight.

She runs off, laughing

VIOLET M. METHLEY

19

I REMEMBER MAMA

KATRIN

Katrin Hanson, eldest daughter of a Norwegian immigrant family now settled in San Francisco, 1910, is writing about her family. She is seated at a desk, smoking a cigarette. She takes up her manuscript and begins to read aloud what she has written

(*Facing the audience—reading*) "For as long as I could remember, the house on Steiner Street had been home. Papa and Mama had both been born in Norway, but they came to San Francisco because Mama's sisters were here. All of us were born here. Nels, the oldest and the only boy—my sister Christine—and the littlest sister, Dagmar." (*She puts down her manuscript and looks out front*) It's funny, but when I look back, I always see Nels and Christine and myself looking almost as we do today. I guess that's because the people you see all the time stay the same age in your head. Dagmar's different. She was always the baby—so I see her as a baby. Even Mama—it's funny, but I always see Mama as around forty. (*She puts out her cigarette, picks up her manuscript and starts to read again*) "Besides us, there was our boarder, Mr Hyde. Mr Hyde was an Englishman who had once been an actor, and Mama was very impressed by his flowery talk and courtly manners. He used to read aloud to us in the evenings. He read us all kinds of books. He thrilled us with *Treasure Island*, and terrified us with *The Hound of the Baskervilles*. I can still remember the horror in his voice. Sometimes he read us poetry. *The Lady of the Lake* and *The Rime of the Ancient Mariner*. There were many nights I couldn't sleep for the way he had set my imagination dancing." But first and foremost, I remember Mama. I remember that every Saturday Mama would sit down by the kitchen table and count out the money Papa had brought home in the little envelope. It wasn't very often that I could get Mama to talk—about herself, of her life in the old country, or what she felt about things. You had to catch her unawares, or when she had nothing to do, which was very, very seldom. I don't think I can ever remember Mama unoccupied.

JOHN VAN DRUTEN

FUTURE MOTHER OF THE RACE

MARLENE TRIPP

Marlene is a bright young "pop" fan. She has a black eye

Fab, it was! Absolutely fab! There they was, the four of them with their guitars. You could see their mouths opening' an' shuttin'—but not a word, not a note! We was all makin' so much noise. "Yeh! Yeh! Yeh!" Coo! What a reception they got! I said to Susie next to me, "Susie," I said, "How'd it be if we could take one of 'em home for a pet?" "Oh, swoons!" she said—an' she did. No—swooned, I meant. Then two p'licemen had to carry her out. After all the trouble we'd had gettin' in. Started to queue as soon as we got the word *they* was comin'. It's no joke, to queue for *six weeks*. Mam got fed-up bringin' me san'wiches an' thermoses—and standin' in for me now an' again. But she's okay, Mam, really. She's a sport. She understands the compulsion of genius, sort of. Cost me six weeks' wages, it did, besides the ticket an' a new anorak— yes, an' a beefsteak for this. (*She touches her eye*) But I don't grudge a pound of it. No—money, not beefsteak.

I often sort of wonder what people used to do in the past—when *they wasn't here*. I mean to say—what did they *do*? I know some of 'em once had that Shakespeare—but then, he wasn't for everybody—if you follow me. In America they got the right idea. In fact, if you think of it most of the right ideas *do* come from America. An' that's another historical question: Whatever did we do before Christopher Robin discovered the place? But I mean to say, in America they're right in orbit. Yeah—oh yeah! They cut up the sheets *they* sleep in at their hotels, an' sell 'em in little bits. *Oooh!* If only they'd do that here! If only! I'd like to buy a bit of *his*! I'd embroider hearts an' kisses all round, and sleep with it under my pillow! I just can't wait! Wonder what his wife thinks about it all? If I was his wife I'd keep him in a cage, I think. Coo! I do love the way you can't see their foreheads for hair. Nor the backs of their necks. Of course, all the boys on the launchin' pad nowadays has their hair done like that—but how *they* wear *theirs*. Of course it was a pity when the ceilin' started comin' down. They said it was the noise we made, but I say it was the jerry-built ceilin'. Besides, they'd been havin' concerts there since Queen Victoria's day, so it was about time, really. Well, the ceilin' started droppin' plaster all over, an' there we was, screechin' away an' takin' no notice. So exalted we was, I don't believe we even noticed just when *they* went. The noise was just the same. I think we was all prepared to die there at the height of our ecstasy. Somebody said afterwards that, for all *they* was heard, we might as well have had the audience *without them*. But some people can talk silly, can't they? So, because we wouldn't move out, the p'lice moved in. A great big one

21

got hold of me. A sergeant. As I said to Susie afterwards: "If you've got to be assaulted, you appreciate it bein' done by somebody better than just a plain bobby." But I don't know where I got this eye. Don't think it was from him, because he'd sort of got me slung over his shoulder an' hangin' down behind. I couldn't do very much. In America, if we'd got the looks, they used to call us dames "toughs". Dunno why. I mean to say, we're not really all that tough, an' I couldn't make no real impression on a great fat back like that. I did pinch him as far down as I could reach. That was when he smacked me on my jeans, which, me bein' that way up, was takin' a mean advantage, sort of. An' not the proper way to treat a lady. Oh, but it was *fab*! The sort of experience you remember to tell your children—if you know what I mean.

A monologue by T. B. MORRIS

THE DIARY OF ANNE FRANK

ANNE FRANK

Mr and Mrs Frank, their two daughters, Anne and Margot; Mr and Mrs Van Daan and their son Peter; and Mr Dussel, are Jews hiding from the Nazis in the top floors of a warehouse in Amsterdam, Holland, during the Second World War—1945. The Van Daan's have been quarrelling and the atmosphere is very tense; Peter, humiliated, goes to his room, Anne follows him and tries to bring him out of his despair

(*Looking up at the skylight*) Look, Peter, the sky. What a lovely day. Aren't the clouds beautiful? You know what I do when it seems as if I couldn't stand being cooped up for one more minute? I *think* myself out. I think myself on a walk in the park where I used to go with Pim. Where the daffodils and the crocus and the violets grow down the slopes. You know the most wonderful thing about *thinking* yourself out? You can have it anyway you like. You can have roses and violets and chrysanthemums all blooming at the same time. It's funny—I used to take it all for granted—and now I've gone crazy about everything to do with Nature. I wish you had a religion, Peter—oh, I don't mean you have to be Orthodox—or believe in heaven and hell and purgatory and things—I just mean—some religion—it doesn't matter what. Just to believe in something. When I think of all that's out there—the trees—the flowers—and seagulls—and when I think of the dearness of you, Peter—and the goodness of the people we know—Mr Kraler, Miep, Dirk, the vegetable man—all risking their lives for us everyday—when I think of these good things, I'm not afraid any more. You know what I sometimes think? I think the world may be going through a phase, the way I was with Mother. It'll pass, maybe not for hundreds of years but some day, I still believe, in spite of everything, that people are really good at heart.

Dramatized by FRANCES GOODRICH and ALBERT HACKETT

CHILDREN IN UNIFORM
MANUELA

Manuela, a highly sensitive child, and Edelgard, are pupils in a Prussian high school. The girls are subjected to strict discipline and all natural desires and emotions are repressed. A teacher, Fraulein Von Bernburg, befriends the girls and they adore her. Manuela develops an affection for her which the headmistress regards as perverted

(*Manuela is stroking Edelgard's hair*) Poor Edelgard! Forget all the horrid things, remember only what's nice—and lovely—Fraulein Von Bernburg— I know she's remote and unapproachable, but that's just what's so wonderful to be able to think about her! Oh, I could do that all day long. To think how she looks, how she speaks. (*Dreamily*) Have you noticed from what a long way off you can hear her step—such a strong, firm, clear tread . . . just like her voice. . . . It's strange, you know, I always think of her as a leader—a ruler. Whenever she comes into the room, or steps on to the teacher's platform, I think of Parliament—or, is she more like a judge? As I watch her my heart nearly stops beating. She makes me feel so afraid. Oh, I don't mean afraid in the way we are afraid of the Head, or Kesten. (*Feeling for the right word*) Awe—is more what I mean. And do you know why? It's because she is unhappy. I feel that she has suffered in some way . . . that . . . there is another side to her quite different from the one she shows us. She can be most frightfully loving . . . (*Edelgard begins to cry so Manuela tickles her and recites to divert her*) Edelgard . . . "Vous, le sang de vingt rois, esclave d'Orosmane. . . ." (*Rising and crossing down left centre*) Oh, Edelgard, I'm so terribly happy, for now I shall be able to show her myself—as I really am! When I'm dressed in my silver armour, with my hair quite free, then, then she will see me properly for the very first time! And you know when someone says those lines:
O brave Nérestan, chevalier genereux,
Vous, qui brisez les fers de tant de malheureux.
Then, then, she must like me. (*Sitting on top of desk down centre, flinging her arms up*) Let me dream I am a knight, a knight who has come to free her—to take her out of this prison, to flee far, far away. Alone, we two, quite alone. (*She stops short and lowers her voice*) Alone? But what good would that be! Whenever I am alone with her I can't say one word! Twenty times I have made up my mind to kiss her hands before doing it once in reality! No, she can't possibly like me! All she sees is a silly dumb idiot before her. If she asks me a question in class, her voice makes me so nervous that everything goes out of my head! And I can only see her hand holding the pencil that is to give me another bad mark, and I hear only that hard "Again nothing learnt!" (*She laughs to herself*) But she hasn't the slightest suspicion how much I learn for her really—or of everything I could do!

CHRISTA WINSLOW

24

GIGI

GIGI

Paris. 1900. Gigi's family: mother, grandmother, and aunt, have shunned the responsibilities of marriage for wealthy and rewarding casual liaisons. Gigi who is now ready to carry on the family tradition is having lessons in deportment, appreciation of jewellery, etc., from her Great-Aunt Alicia, a most successful courtesan

(*Aunt Alicia enters from the bedroom, Gigi curtsies*) Oh, good afternoon, Aunt Alicia. You've got your headache again, Aunt, haven't you? I always know, because you wear that lace thing on your hair. (*Hopefully*) As you have a headache, Aunt, perhaps I won't have to—I mean, perhaps you don't want to give me my lesson today. Oh, thank you, Aunt. (*Gigi picks up her gloves and strides to the door*) I don't want to sit down, Aunt, I'm not in the least bit tired. I came over in a car. (*With her usual excitement*) Yes. In Tonton's de Dion-Bouton landaulette. He's at the house with Grandmama now. (*She rushes to the windows*) Yes. He didn't go to the Flower Fête in Nice this year because he's broken it off with Liane. (*She leans out of the window and calls*) Albert! He's broken it off with Liane. (*She calls again*) Oh Albert! Don't go away, I'm riding back with you. (*Gigi being pulled away from the window by her aunt*) I'm sorry, Aunt. (*She puts an arm round her aunt's shoulder*) Oh, Aunt, you should have seen me driving here. The whole time I was in the automobile I put on a martyred expression like this—(*very bored*). As if I was bored to death with luxurious living. But I could see people watching. And at the Eiffel Tower a very elegant man tipped his hat—to me. (*Thrilled*) Oh! It was just as if I'd suddenly grown up to be a fashionable young lady. Well, good-bye, Aunt. (*She picks up her gloves and moves towards the door*) Please watch me from the window as I drive off, will you. But I . . . Aunt . . . (*Aunt Alicia indicates a chair and Gigi has to sit*) Yes, Aunt. Tonton and Liane have broken it off; and of course it worries me. If Tonton makes friends with a new lady he won't have time to come and play piquet with us any more, or drink camomile tea. At least not for some time. (*Simply*) That would be a shame. Well—but I'm not supposed to repeat gossip, am I! Well, one of the girls at school, Lydia Poret, has a mother who goes skating every day at the Palais de Glace. She heard all about it there. She says Liane merely waited for her birthday present and then skipped off. She tried to hide in a tiny village in Normandy. But it wasn't hard for Tonton to find out that there were only two bedrooms at the inn, and that Liane was in one of them, and a skating instructor named Sandomar, in the other. Tonton gave Liane a string of thirty-seven monstrous pearls. The one in the middle is as big as Mme Poret's thumb. (*She attempts to indicate the size*) Oh Mme Poret said Tonton had tried to give Liane a string of small pearls; but then she absolutely demanded those monsters. (*Gigi rises, kisses Aunt Alicia and moves to the door*) Well, good-bye, Aunt. Until next week. Now I can have a game of piquet with Tonton. Of course Tonton is at home with grandmama having at least two cups of camomile tea. He can't leave without his car. Well, until next Sunday, Aunt Alicia. (*Gigi turns to go through the door when her aunt calls her name. Gigi turns*) Oh Aunt! Oh, no, but Aunt . . . (*As Aunt Alicia goes to her bedroom, Gigi is left alone. She is in a bad temper. She jumps up and down; throws her gloves on the floor; kicks a chair, and hurts her toe*) Hells bells and bloody cauliflowers!

COLETTE AND ANITA LOOS

CALL IT A DAY

ANN

Ann Hilton, fifteen years old, with a highly intelligent little face, enters her parents' bedroom. It is about 8 a.m.

I say, Mum, I do think you might speak to Cath—she's bagged the bathroom first again. She's got the tap full on. Oh dear, and I did want to be extra early this morning. I'm sure I've got one of the algebra questions down wrong. (*She sits on the side of Dorothy's—her mother—bed*) Mum— can you think of any possible use algebra can be in one's after-life? I mean, after school life. After I've done half an hour's algebra my brain feels most peculiar—sort of floating. Are you keen on having a daughter with a floating brain? If I could get off algebra, I could spend more time on really important things—like poetry. I've been reading Rossetti. Oh, Mum—he's the most lovely poet. I've been reading him since six this morning. The early morning's the best time for poetry—when everything's fresh. The words get right inside you and your mind's so clear it's like— like crystal water. It's lovely to read aloud. (*Hurrying across to her father's bathroom door, but not opening it*) I say, Daddy—would you like to hurry and lend me your bathroom? Would you? But, darling, wouldn't you like to shave in your dressing-room? Oh, do be a sport, Daddy. Cath's bagged the bathroom and I'm terribly late and—oh, darling—you *are* a pet rabbit. (*To her mother*) He's going to let me. Whoops of joy. I'll only be a few minutes. Honest—oh, you don't really mind, do you? (*She flings herself at her mother*) Darling Mummy face. But it's a term of endearment. Anyhow, Egyptian mummies are lovely—all queer and mysterious. (*With sudden complete self-absorption*) Mummy, do you think I'm psychic? Well, I'm always feeling as if I ought to be able to see things. I expect it's because I'm sensitive. (*She picks up her mother's hand-mirror*) I've got a sensitive mouth, haven't I, Mummy? Oh, Mummy, I do think you're unromantic, just when I was talking about important things. You're always shrivelling me up. Do you know what I read in the paper yesterday? Girls of my age are like sensitive plants. Mummy, can I have the weeniest squeedge of your bath salts? I'll only take one grain.

DODIE SMITH

27

CHARADE

IRIS

Iris, the parlourmaid who is very, very sure of herself, is breathlessly excited. She talks to Cook and the kitchenmaid, Ivy. The scene takes place in the servants' room

This is a red-letter day for me. All I've got to do is to play my cards right, and this afternoon sees the turning point of my whole career! You wait, Cook, just you wait! Why, this time next year I'll be bathing in champagne! You see if I'm not! I'm going on the films—and what's more, you're going to help me there! I've planned it all out—up in my room, just now—and, oh, Cook, it really is my chance at last—and you will help me, won't you?— You won't let me down? I've thought out a lovely new name for myself— Melody Dawne! What d'you think of that for a glamour-name, eh? Melody Dawne—and I'm going on the films! And it's all through the lady that's been lunching with Madam today—Miss Rosa Rosario, the famous woman film-producer. And she's waiting to start on a lovely new film, and she was going on to Madam about it all through lunch, and I couldn't help hearing. Listen to this, because this is the bit where I come in! "Here we are, all ready to begin," she said to Madam, "and everything held up on account of one part. Quite a small part," she said, "but very important. And it's *got* to be the right type. We've combed London from end to end," she said, "and so far we haven't found a single actress who comes within a mile of it." And then—and then—Cook, she said this: "We're so desperate, Janet," she said, "that if we could find someone who'd never acted before, but who was *right* for the part, we'd take her and train her for it." There now! And a bit later, I caught her looking at me sort of sideways, and I heard her whisper to Madam, "What an extremely pretty girl." (*She pauses for Cook to make some remark, but Cook does not oblige*) Meaning me, Cook. So you see. It's my chance. When Miss Rosario sees me acting, she'll know her search is ended, and she'll give me the part at once! I don't mind if it is only a small part, just to begin. You wait till a year from now! Melody Dawne! That'll be me! I've been practising for weeks and weeks in my bedroom, Cook, and I act beautifully! I do really! Listen to this! (*Moving a few paces away—halting—flinging her arms out wide—reciting with terrific dramatic emphasis*) "The quality of mercy is not strained! it droppeth as the gentle rain from . . . (*She pauses—raising her right arm—pointing to the ceiling*) Heaven, upon the earth . . . (*She pauses—thrusting her left arm downwards —pointing to the floor*) beneath!" There! What d'you think of that? All *right*! But you wait till Miss Rosario sees me, that's all. She'll think very different. Madam's going to show her all over the house, this afternoon. Oh, Cook, I've planned it out beautifully—and what I want you to do is act a little scene with me, that's all—so she can see at a glance how talented I am. Oh, you will, won't you, Cook, you will help me, *please*? PHILIP JOHNSON

28

I CAPTURE THE CASTLE

CASSANDRA

The Mortmains, father, step-mother, and two daughters, live in an ancient crumbling castle, and they have no money. The eldest daughter, Rose, bewails their poverty and the dearth of eligible young men; but Cassandra is not yet interested in men, being wholly absorbed in training herself to be a writer by recording their family fortunes in her journal

(*Cassandra opens her journal, but instead of writing she soliloquizes*) Do I really want to hold my Midsummer rites, now Rose isn't here? How well I remember the first year I held them—after the Vicar told me that Ancient Britons may have held them on our mound. Was I eight or nine? How frightened we were, up on the mound, Rose and I, and how we enjoyed being frightened. Do I still believe that strange things are about on Midsummer Eve? Elementals—Spirits of Earth and Fire and Water? Prehistoric people believed in them, and worshipped them. Perhaps things that countless people believe in become real. I'm sure there's magic in the air tonight.

(*Sternly*) Cassandra Mortmain, what you're really thinking about has nothing to do with magic, you're remembering Stephen very nearly kissed you a few minutes ago—and you very nearly wanted him to. And yet not half an hour ago, you wondered if you weren't in love with Neil—who will never have any more to do with you because you helped Rose land Simon. What a common expression. (*As she continues she collects what she needs for the rites*) How different the house feels when I'm alone. It seems to belong to me more—I even belong to myself more than I usually do. I am me. This arm I move is mine. How pleasant to wave it through the unresisting air. (*She crosses to the sink, picks up a garland of wild flowers, puts the garland around her neck. She quotes*)
> I know a bank where on the wild thyme blows,
> Where oxlips and the nodding violet grows . . .

She picks up a fallen flower

> Fetch me that flower; the herb I showed thee once;
> The juice of it on sleeping eyelids laid
> Will make a man or woman madly dote
> Upon the next live creature that it sees.

She touches her eyelids with the flower

I hope I don't meet one of Mr Stebbins's horses.

She picks up the basket and crosses by the open moat door

DODIE SMITH

CHARADE

ROSA ROSARIO

Rosa Rosario, a film producer, is a great "talker". Janet Colyngham, the mistress of the house, is showing Rosa over her property. They enter the servants' room

"The whole *thing*," as I said to Monty only last Tuesday—or it may have been Wednesday—"The whole *thing*," as I said, "is a question of *type*! Give me the *type*," I said, "and I'll give you your film! But I cannot make bricks without straw, and you must not expect me to! And it's no use coming to me with a long face, Monty darling," I said, "and telling me that the delay's costing two hundred pounds a day! I don't care if it's costing two thousand! I don't care—(*snapping her fingers*)—that much. No, no, no," I said, "not one inch of film will I shoot, until my artistic sense tells me that I've got the right woman for the part, the right *type!*"— You do see what I mean, Janet dear, don't you? The utterly, utterly, utterly right *type!* I've combed the whole of London, literally *combed* it, and I'm prepared to comb the whole of England, too. Of course, the country's stiff with women who are aching to go on the films, God knows why! Stiff with them! Oh, I know! I know! Their letters lie on my desk like a snowdrift! But what use are they to me, if they're not the right *type*? Fat, thin, short, or tall, they might just as well be at the bottom of the sea. As I said to Monty, "If they're the *wrong* type," I said, "don't waste my time with them, *please!*"—You do follow me, Janet, don't you? (*Rosa becomes aware of Iris, the parlourmaid, and points to her*) Now—now, you take that girl over there, for instance. (*Going to Iris*) Now, you probably want to go on the films. (*Turning back to Janet*) *She* stands about as much chance as she does of flying to the moon. (*Twisting Iris round*) Take a look at her! Front! Side! Back! There you are! Goodish figure! Pretty! But in the same way that billions of other girls are pretty! Billions! She isn't just the *wrong* type! She's no type at all! (*Rosa looses interest in Iris and turns suddenly to the Cook*) Now take this woman here! Stand up please! Up! Let me look at you! Now, this woman I *might* use—at a pinch! A down-and-out in a dockside-pub scene, or a drunken old flower-woman in a fog. She's a type, but not *the* type! Oh, dear, no. (*To Cook*) Sit down, please. You see, Janet, how maddeningly difficult it all is! This needle in a haystack that I've *got* to find! Where is she? Where? Echo answers with that one word—"*Where?*" Of course, it's only a small part, but it's the most tense and vital moment of the whole film! In fact, it's the most stupendous moment in any film I've ever done! Just try to imagine the situation, dear! The scene's as it might be in this very room, and here they are, waiting, holding their breaths, wondering what's going to happen next, when, suddenly, the door (*pointing to door*) *that* door, begins slowly to open, and—and *she* comes in! The *woman!*

As she says these words Mrs Lockett, the charwoman, enters carrying her empty pail

Rosa freezes into a sudden silence, as she follows with her eyes the drab and undramatic figure. And then:

Who is she? (*Louder*) Janet! That woman! Who is she? (*Hurrying after Mrs Lockett*) You—you with the bucket! Come here, please! Quickly! I want you! (*To her—her excitement increasing*) Stand there! Don't move! Let me look at you! (*Stepping back to study her better—then clasping her hands ecstatically*) But, Janet—she's *it*. She's absolutely *it!* Why, she's what I've been searching for all over London! (*She takes another step back*) Oh, *yes!* Janet, I've found her at *last!*

PHILIP JOHNSON

GREEN MANSIONS
RIMA

Green Mansions (trees of the tropical forest) is set in the Venezuelan forest. Rima is young, beautiful, a mysterious "spirit", a captivating "bird-woman", protector of animals, snakes and birds, who lives in the forest with her grandfather. Abel, an explorer, first encounters Rima when she stops him from stoning a snake; they soon fall in love

O Mother, Mother, listen to me, to Rima, your beloved child! All these years I have been wickedly deceived by grandfather—Nufflo—the old man that found you. Often have I spoken to him of Riolama, where you once were, and your people are, and he denied all knowledge of such a place. Sometimes he said that it was at an immense distance, in a great wilderness full of serpents larger than the trunks of great trees, and of evil spirits and savage men, slayers of all strangers. At other times he affirmed that no such place existed; that it was a tale told by the Indians; such false things did he say to me—to Rima, your child. O Mother, can you believe such wickedness? Then a stranger, a white man from Venezuela, came into our woods: this is the man that was bitten by a serpent, and his name is Abel: only I do not call him by that name, but by other names which I have told you. But perhaps you did not listen, or did not hear, for I spoke softly, and not as now, on my knees, solemnly. For I must tell you, O Mother, that after you died the Priest at Voa told me repeatedly that when I prayed, whether to you or to the Mother of Heaven, I must speak as he had taught me, if I wished to be heard and understood. And that was most strange, since you had taught me differently; but you were living then, at Voa, and now you are in Heaven perhaps you know better. Therefore listen to me now, O Mother, and let nothing I say escape you. When this white man had been for some days with us a strange thing happened to me, which made me different, so that I was no longer Rima, although Rima still—so strange was this thing; and I often went to the pool to look at myself and see the change in me, but nothing different could I see. In the first place it came from his eyes passing into mine, and filling me just as the lightning fills a cloud at sunset: afterwards it was no longer from his eyes only, but it came into me whenever I saw him, even at a distance, when I heard his voice, and most of all when he touched me with his hand. When he is out of my sight I cannot rest until I see him again; and when I see him then I am glad, yet in such fear and trouble that I hide myself from him. O Mother, it could not be told; for once when he caught me in his arms and compelled me to speak of it he did not understand; yet there was need to tell it; then it came to me that only to our people could it be told, for they would understand, and reply to me, and tell me what to do in such a case.   W. H. HUDSON

From the novel

THE WILD DUCK

HEDVIG

Hedvig, a quiet, sensitive child, is retouching a photograph. Her father, Hjalmar, and her grandfather, Old Ekdal, are occupied in the attic. Someone knocks at the hall door, Hedvig does not notice it. Gregers Werle comes in and stands for a moment by the door

(*Turning and going towards him*) Good morning. Do come in, please. I'll go and tell them. (*Gregers tells her not to go and she settles down to her work while Gregers watches her in silence*) It's so untidy here. I'm helping Daddy with a little job. No, I don't go to school any more. Because Daddy's afraid I shall hurt my eyes. He's promised to give me lessons, but he hasn't had time for it yet. When I can manage to I spend a good deal of time in the attic, it's like a world of its own, absolutely its own! And then there are such lots of wonderful things. There are big cupboards with books in them; and there are pictures in a lot of the books. And then there's an old cabinet with drawers and partitions in it; and a big clock with figures that are supposed to come out. But the clock doesn't go any more. And then there's an old paint-box and things like that. And then all the books. Most of them are in English, and I don't understand that. But then I look at the pictures. There is one very large book that is called *Harryson's History of London*; that must be quite a hundred years old. And there are a tremendous lot of pictures in that. At the beginning there's a picture of Death with an hour-glass and a girl. I think that's dreadful. But then there are all the other pictures with churches and castles and streets and great ships sailing on the sea. An old sea captain lived here once and he brought them home. They called him "The Flying Dutchman". And that's queer because he wasn't a Dutchman at all. But in the end he didn't come back, and he left everything behind him.

I want to stay at home here always and help Daddy and Mother. I'd like most of all to learn to engrave pictures like those in the English books. But I don't think Daddy likes it. Daddy's so odd about things like that. Just think, he talks about my learning basket-weaving and straw-plaiting! But I don't see that there's anything in *that*. But Daddy's right in one thing. If I'd learnt to weave baskets, then I could have made the new basket for the wild duck. It's all so strange about the wild duck. There's no-one who knows her. And no-one who knows where she's come from, either.

HENRIK IBSEN

33

MINOR MURDER

CARLA

Two cousins, Margaret and Carla, long to run away from home together and finish a book they are writing. Both the girls are on edge, and their relationship is a strange, unhealthy one. Margaret's mother—Shirley Field—announces that the girls are to be separated and Margaret will go to a boarding-school. Margaret bursts into a violent rage, and attacks her mother. Left alone the girls plot, and eventually put into action the murder of Margaret's mother

(*Carla rises and moves away thoughtfully*) Let's imagine we're trying to work out a plot for a new book. A sort of mystery story. Now concentrate. This is an imaginary situation. Two girls—they're the heroines in the book—want to get rid of the mother of one of them—a hateful mother, like yours —so as to inherit her property. They must be so clever that nobody suspects them. (*Sitting beside Margaret*) How could it be done? No, drowning in a bath tub won't work. Because the lady of the house always locks the bathroom door when she has her bath. Even if the girls could think of a way to get her to open the door, she'd be out of the bath. A car accident is a good idea, but the trouble with that is that people aren't always killed. The girls—in the book—would want to be sure that their victim would die. Well, doctors always test for poison. They recognize symptoms. No, all these ideas are too complicated. It must be something simple. Like a fall. They could hit her with something, all it would take would be a blow on the back of the head. One blow—with something sharp. Like a flintstone. I think I've got it. Suppose there was a collection like this. (*Carla jumps up and turns to the cabinet which houses a collection of weapons*) While your mother was being so cruel to you that hatchet there caught my eye. I could hardly resist grabbing it and striking her with it. (*She goes to the cabinet and takes out the axe*) Look at this thing. One good blow would be enough. It's perfect. (*Moves to sofa*) The police would think the wound was from a rock in the garden. In any case, our heroines could wipe it clean. Suppose she saw a piece of jewellery in one of the flower beds. She'd be certain to lean over to get it. (*Carla now speaks in a hard practical voice*) Right. Well, there's plenty of time to work out the details. Aunt Shirley will leave the house and walk down through the rock garden to the garage. She won't miss the church bazaar. We'll set it all up for next Tuesday. Agreed? Oh! Let's stop pretending, Meg; of course it's for real. It's our only hope. What's right? What's wrong? Who cares? You've got to grow up, Meg. They don't hang girls our age. Anyhow, they won't find out. We'll be too clever. We'll be able to do what we like. We can travel. We can go on writing books. We'll both be orphans, so there'll be nobody to boss us around. We can be together all our lives. Of course, I wouldn't suggest all this if she weren't destroying our happiness. But she is. Keep saying I hate her. Hate her. She doesn't deserve to live. And then we'll never leave each other. We could never risk leaving each other. This is a secret that will bind us together for always.

REGINALD DENHAM and MARY ORR

FIGURE OF FUN

MURIEL

Muriel is a young maid, her employer is an actor

(*Muriel enters, she is carrying an opened letter. She looks very worried*) Oh!
(*She re-reads a portion of the letter*) Oh dear, oh dear, oh dear. (*She finishes
reading the letter then gazes into space in consternation. She glances at her
wrist-watch, then crosses to the telephone, lifts the receiver and dials a
number. As she waits for a reply, she carries the telephone to the easy chair,
sits and sings softly to herself*) I often sit and wonder—why I appeal to
men, I often sit and wonder . . . (*Suddenly into the telephone*) Ruby? . . .
Oh—Mabel? . . . It's me, Muriel. Isn't Ruby back yet? . . . Oh, well,
she's got further to come. I've only just got in—I nipped on a thirty-eight
from Piccadilly. (*With a note of drama*) 'Ere you know where me and
Ruby've been tonight? . . . Oh! Well, Mr Tracey give me two tickets to
go and see him in "Figure of Fun" FIGURE OF FUN. He's acting in it. . . .
(*Exasperated*) No, it isn't—it's a play. Honest, Mabel, you're so slow.
'Ow you ever got a job in a post office—I don't know. Well, anyway . . .
Oh, is she? Let me speak to her will you? . . . Ruby? . . . It's me, Muriel.
You got home quick . . . a lift? . . . Did you? Well, something chronic's
'appened. I come in, don't see Mrs Tracey anywhere, I go into the kitchen
to get Mr Tracey's supper ready, and I'm just thinking I'll make him a
chocolate soufflé as a bit of a surprise—you know, sort of to thank him for
buying us the seats tonight, when what do I see propped up on the fridge
but a letter. It's for me, from Mrs Tracey. Listen to this . . . Oh! listen.
(*She reads the letter*) "Dear Muriel, I am enclosing a letter which I want
you to give the master when he comes home from the theatre. You've
always been so kind, and thoughtful that I feel it's only right to let you
know what's going on. I'm sorry to have to tell you that I'm leaving Mr
Tracey——" (*She breaks off*) What? . . . You'll be what? . . . That's just
what I said to myself, but I'm surprised a nice girl like you even *knows* the
expression. (*She reads*) "I am enclosing this letter for you to give him, I
am leaving Mr Tracey, but I haven't got the courage to tell him myself.
I'm afraid it will be a shock, so please don't give it to him if he comes back
from the theatre alone, but I have an idea he's bringing some friends
back, and I expect Mr Jarvis, will be there." That's Guy Jarvis, the one
that acts Edgar in the play. (*She reads*) "So if he is, will you give the letter
to Mr Jarvis, explain what it's about, and ask him to give it to my husband.
I am so sorry to give you this trouble, thank you for everything, and I'm
enclosing a little present for you." (*Matter of factly*) A couple of smackers!
(*Seriously*) Well, that's a bit of all right, isn't it? . . . She's left him. Of
course, it doesn't surprise me. She's French, you know. . . . Yes, what
I'm wondering is, what if he comes back alone. What am I supposed to

36

do? He's always been so nice, Mr Tracey. Friendly, always the gentleman—
quite turned me when I read the letter. She didn't ought to have left him
like that, and leaving me to . . . (*Suddenly*) . . . 'ere he is . . .

ANDRÉ ROUSSIN

FIVE FINGER EXERCISE
PAMELA

Louise Harrington, Pamela's mother, has engaged a young German, Walter Langer, as tutor to her daughter. Langer's stay in the Harrington family begins favourably: his pupil likes him, and his talents make him welcome to Louise and her son Clive. But the Harringtons are a desperately unhappy family

(*Walter and Pamela are sitting at the breakfast table. The girl, in her dressing-gown, is reading one of the better Sunday papers*) Walter, what does "Salacious" mean? Salacious—it's in this article. Wise? Does it? I suppose I should have guessed. You ought to teach English. I'm sure you'd be miles better than the man at my last school. Anyway, he was a Dutchman. Mother says this is the only Sunday paper she'll have in the house. I think it's mean of her. Everyone else has the popular ones with pictures of rapes . . . (*Impulsively*) Are you happy here? Are you really, really happy? Who do you like best? No, seriously. Clive? Is Clive very unhappy? That's because he was spoilt when he was young. You know—to spoil someone. Like damage. (*Drinking her coffee*) I'm sure he ought to get married. For some people it's the best thing. You must help him find a girl. There was a girl once, a girl called Peggy-Ann who worked in the tobacconist's when we were in the Isle of Wight. She used to wear leopard-skin trousers and great sort of brass bells in her ears. Clive said they used to go down on the beach and neck, but I bet he was just bragging. So you see, you've got to help him. I'm sure you know hundreds of girls. At home everyone keeps on at him but no-one really takes any notice of him. (*Brightly*) Clive spends his whole time not being listened to. Well of course you can't expect Mother to listen. No mother ever really listens to her children. It's not done. Poor Clive. You know, they really only use him to help them when they're rowing. With Mother and Daddy the row is never really *about*—well, what they're quarrelling about. I mean . . . behind what they say you can feel—well, that Mother did this in the past, and Daddy did that. I don't mean anything *particular*. . . . (*She stops, confused*) Oh, dear . . . I think marriage is a very difficult subject, don't you? (*Pursuing her own thought*) I mean, who begins things? Do you see? I know Mother's frightful to him about culture, and uses music and things to keep him out—which is terrible. But isn't that just because *he* made *her* keep out of things when they were first married? You know he wouldn't even let her go to concerts and theatres although she was dying to, and once he threw a picture she'd bought into the dustbin; one of those modern things, all squiggles and blobs. (*Gestures*) . . . But then, mightn't *that* just have been because being brought up by himself he was afraid of making a fool of himself. Oh, poor Daddy. . . . Poor Mother, too. (*To him, brightly*) You know, I shouldn't wonder if parents don't turn out to be my hobby when I grow up.

PETER SHAFFER

DEAR BRUTUS

MARGARET

*Second chances in life are rare, but in this play three couples, two single
ladies and the butler, Matey, (who are staying in a strange country house
owned by a lovable but mysterious character called Lob) are granted their
secret wishes when they enter an enchanted wood on Midsummer Eve. Mr
Dearth, who in reality is ill-matched with his wife, has no children, and is a
failed artist; in the wood he lives the life of a successful artist and the proud
father of Margaret*

(*Margaret comes racing on to find the spot where the easel was put up last
night*) Daddy, Daddy. I have won. Here is the place. (*Dearth comes in.
The easel is erected, Margaret helping by getting in the way. Margaret is
critical, as an artist's daughter should be*) The moon is rather pale tonight,
isn't she? (*Showing off*) Daddy, watch me, look at me. Please, sweet
moon, a pleasant expression. No, no, not as if you were sitting for it;
that is too professional. That is better; thank you. Now keep it. That is
the sort of thing you say to them, Dad. (*Pelting him with nuts*) I can't
sleep when the moon's at the full; she keeps calling to me to get up.
Perhaps I am *her* daughter too. Paint me into the picture as well as
Mamma? You could call it "A Mother and Daughter" or simply "Two
Ladies", if the moon thinks that calling me her daughter would make
her seem too old. (*Emerging in an unexpected place*) Daddy, do you really
prefer her. (*Considering the picture*) And what a moon! Dad she is not
quite so fine as that. (*She sees Mr Coade, another of the guests from the
house, pirouetting round and dancing with happiness and playing on a whistle.
Margaret imitates him. Suddenly Margaret's mood changes, she clings to her
father*) Hold me tight, Daddy, I'm frightened. I think they want to take
you away from me. It's too lovely, Daddy; I won't be able to keep hold
of it. The world—everything—and you, Daddy, most of all. Things that are
too beautiful can't last. (*Still in his arms*) Daddy, am I sometimes stranger
than other people's daughters? (*Solemnly*) Do you think I am sometimes
too full of gladness? (*Dearth is at his easel again. Margaret persisting*)
To be very gay, dearest dear, is so near to being very sad. (*Unexpectedly*)
Daddy, what is a "might-have-been"? How awful it would be, Daddy,
to wake up and find one wasn't alive. Daddy, wouldn't it be awful? I
think men need daughters. Especially artists. (*Covering herself with leaves
and kicking them off*) Fame is not everything. Daughters are the thing. I
wonder if sons would be even nicer? Sons are not so bad. Signed M.
Dearth. But I'm glad you prefer daughters. (*She works her way toward
him on her knees*) At what age are we nicest, Daddy? (*She constantly has
to repeat her question, as Dearth is so engaged with his moon*) Hie, Daddy
at what age are we nicest? Daddy, hie, hie, at what age are we nicest?

39

The year before she puts up her hair. But there's a nicer year coming to you. Daddy, there is a nicer year coming to you. The year she does put up her hair! You will never know whether I am a girl or a woman till you look at my hair. And even then you won't know, for if it is down I shall put it up, and if it is up I shall put it down. And so my daddy will gradually get used to the idea. (*Gleaming*) Shut your eyes, Dad, and I shall give you a glimpse into the future. Shut your eyes, please. Please, Daddy. Don't open them till I tell you. (*On her knees among the leaves*) Daddy, now I am putting up my hair. I have got such a darling of a mirror. It is such a darling mirror I've got, Dad. Dad, don't look. I shall tell you about it. It is a little pool of water. I wish we could take it home and hang it up. Of course the moment my hair is up there will be other changes also; for instance, I shall talk quite differently. I am just preparing you. You see, darling, I can't call you Dad when my hair is up. I think I shall call you Parent. Parent dear, do you remember the days when your Margaret was a slip of a girl, and sat on your knee? How foolish we were, Parent, in those distant days. Now I must be more distant to you; more like a boy who could not sit on your knee any more. I am not quite sure whether I want you to look. It makes such a difference. Perhaps you won't know me. Even the pool is looking a little scared. (*The change in her voice makes him open his eyes quickly. She confronts him shyly*) What do you think? Will I do?

J. M. BARRIE

THE BUSINESS OF GOOD GOVERNMENT

HOSTESS

The Business of Good Government *is a nativity play. The Hostess owns "The Bethlehem Inn"*

(*The Hostess comes forward with a broom, sweeping busily, talking to the audience as she does so*) It's not as if they were all paying for their rooms neither—half of 'em come here with a piece of yellow paper—"A Government chit, madam, it'll be charged to your credit from the beginning of the next Revenue Period—take it to the Town Hall". The way my house is at the moment, you'd think *I* was running the Town Hall. Civil Servants. . . . Then there's the military—they don't pay neither. "Haw, haw, landlady, I want accommodation for a corporal and thirteen men of Number Eight Detail, three nights altogether, breakfasts and suppers, find their own dinners: but you'll have to provide cooking facilities . . . oh yes, and covered storage for the transport. See the place is clean." Oh, I could lie down and die! To say nothing of the rest of 'em. "Have you got a room, please?" "Could you let us have a bed, missus?" "Just a corner, just a mattress, just a bit of straw—every house in the place is full, we've been all round the town." I know very well they're full. *I'm full!* No vacancies! Not any more. I mean it. Why should I have my premises made a scapegoat for administrative incompetence and I don't care who hears me! (*Shaking her broom angrily at the Angel*) I am perfectly aware that the decree has gone out from Caesar Augustus, young man. That's exactly what I mean. All done as usual with no thought whatever for the convenience of individuals. . . . Where was I? Oh, yes, administrative incompetence. There's more to it than that, you know. It's not just incompetence—it's the downright inhumanity that makes me so upset.

Joseph and Mary enter

The Hostess half turns and points them out to the audience

This poor girl from the north—all that long way in such terrible weather and the baby due any minute. . . . What do they expect me to do? I haven't a room in the house. (*She turns and speaks to Mary*) What do you expect me to do, dear? I don't know whether I'm on my head or me heels—just look at the place, all chockablock and I'm run off me feet! You'll have to find somewhere else.

JOHN ARDEN and MARGARETTA D'ARCY

41

THE RIVALS

LUCY

Lucy, a maid and general go-between, is assessing her wealth and cleverness

Ha! Ha! Ha!—So, my dear Simplicity, let me give you a little respite. (*Altering her manner*) Let girls in my station be as fond as they please of appearing expert, and knowing in their trusts; commend me to a mask of silliness, and a pair of sharp eyes for my own interest under it!—Let me see to what account have I turned my simplicity lately. (*Looks at a paper*) For abetting Miss Lydia Languish in a design of running away with an ensign!—In money, sundry times, twelve pounds twelve; gowns, five; hats, ruffles, caps, etc.; etc.; numberless!—From the said ensign, within this last month, six guineas and a half. About a quarter's pay!—Item, from Mrs Malaprop, for betraying the young people to her—when I found matters were likely to be discovered—two guineas and a black paduasoy.—Item, from Mr Acres, for carrying divers letters—which I never delivered—two guineas and a pair of buckles.—Item, from Sir Lucius O'Trigger, three crowns, two gold pocket-pieces, and a silver snuff-box!—Well done, Simplicity!—Yet I was forced to make my Hibernian believe that he was corresponding, not with the aunt, but with the niece; for though not over rich, I found he had too much pride and delicacy to sacrifice the feelings of a gentleman to the necessities of his fortune.

R. B. SHERIDAN

THE LARK

JOAN

Joan tells her story from the very beginning

I like remembering the beginning: at home, in the fields, when I was still a little girl looking after the sheep, the first time I heard the Voices, that is what I like to remember. . . . It is after the evening Angelus. I am very small and my hair is still in pigtails. I am sitting in the field, thinking of nothing at all. God is good and keeps me safe and happy, close to my mother and my father and my brother, in the quiet countryside of Domremy, while the English soldiers are looting and burning villages up and down the land. My big sheep-dog is lying with his head in my lap; and suddenly I feel his body ripple and tremble, and a hand seems to have touched my shoulder, though I know no-one has touched me. I turned to look. A great light was filling the shadows behind me. The voice was gentle and grave. I had never heard it before, and all it said to me was: "Be a good and sensible child, and go often to church." But I *was* good, and I *did* go to church often, and I showed I was sensible by running away to safety. That was all that happened the first time. And I didn't say anything about it when I got home; but after summer I went back. The moon was rising; it shone on the white sheep; and that was all the light there was. And then came the second time; the bells were ringing for the noonday Angelus. The light came again, in bright sunlight, but brighter than the sun, and that time I saw him. A man in a white robe, with two white wings reaching from the sky to the ground. He didn't tell me his name that day, but later on I found out that he was the blessed St Michael. (*In the deep voice of the Archangel*)—"Joan, go to the help of the King of France, and give him back his kingdom." (*She replies in her own voice*) Oh sir, you haven't looked at me; I am only a young peasant girl, not a great captain who can lead an army. "You will go and search out Robert de Beaudricourt, the Governor of Vaucouleurs. He will give you a suit of clothes to dress you like a man, and he will take you to the Dauphin. St Catherine and St Margaret will protect you." (*She suddenly drops to the floor sobbing with fear*) Please, please pity me, holy sir! I'm a little girl; I'm happy here alone in the fields. I've never had to be responsible for anything, except my sheep. The Kingdom of France is far beyond anything I can do. If you will only look at me you will see I am small, and ignorant. The realm of France is too heavy, sir. But the King of France has famous captains, as strong as you could need and they're used to doing these things. If they lose a battle they sleep as soundly as ever. They simply say the snow or the wind was against them; and they just cross all the dead men off their roll. But I should always remember I had killed them. Please have pity on me! . . . No such thing. No pity. He had gone already, and there I was, with France on my shoulders.   JEAN ANOUILH

43

PYGMALION

ELIZA DOOLITTLE

Eliza, a flower-girl, has come to Professor Henry Higgins for speech lessons. Colonel Pickering has challenged Higgins to pass Eliza off as a Duchess at the end of six months. Higgins accepts the challenge. Eliza's father, Alfred Doolittle, arrives, hoping to get something out of Eliza's sudden good fortune. Higgins gives him a five-pound note, and suggests that he comes to visit his daughter regularly, whereupon Alfred declines on the pretext of having a job

Don't you believe the old liar. He'd as soon you set a bulldog on him as a clergyman. You won't see him again in a hurry. I don't want never to see him again, I don't. He's a disgrace to me, he is, collecting dust instead of working at his trade. Taking money out of other people's pockets into his own. His proper trade's a navvy; and he works at it sometimes too— for exercise—and earns good money at it. Aint you going to call me Miss Doolittle any more? Oh; I don't mind; only it sounded so genteel. I should just like to take a taxi to the corner of Tottenham Court Road and get out there and tell it to wait for me; just to put the girls in their place a bit. I wouldn't speak to them, you know. Well; you don't call the like of them my friends now, I should hope. They've took it out of me often enough with their ridicule when they had the chance; and now I means to get a bit of me own back. But if I'm to have fashionable clothes, I'll wait. I should like to have some. Mrs Pearce says you're going to give me some to wear in bed at night different to what I wear in the day-time; but it do seem a waste of money when you could get something to show. Besides, I never could fancy changing in cold things on a winter night. Ah—ow—oo—oh. (*She rushes out*)

GEORGE BERNARD SHAW

PRIDE AND PREJUDICE

LYDIA

Elizabeth and Jane Bennet have joined their sisters Kitty and Lydia, and all are returning by carriage to their home—Longbourn

How nicely we are crammed in, I am glad I bought my bonnet, if it is only for the fun of having another bandbox! Well, now let us be quite comfortable and snug, and talk and laugh all the way home. And in the first place, let us hear what has happened to you all since you went away. Have you seen any pleasant men? Have you had any flirting? I was in great hopes that one of you would have got a husband before you came back. Jane will be quite an old maid soon, I declare. She is almost three and twenty! Lord, how ashamed I should be of not being married before three and twenty! My Aunt Philips wants you so to get husbands, you can't think. She says Lizzy had better have taken Mr Collins; but I do not think there would have been any fun in it. Lord! How I should like to be married before any of you! And then I would chaperon you about to all the balls. Dear me! We had such a good piece of fun the other day at Colonel Forster's. Kitty and me were to spend the day there, and Mrs Forster promised to have a little dance in the evening (by the bye, Mrs Forster and me are *such* friends!); and so she asked the two Harringtons to come, but Harriet was ill, and so Pen was forced to come by herself; and then, what do you think we did? We dressed Chamberlayne in woman's clothes on purpose to pass for a lady—only think what fun! Not a soul knew of it, but Colonel and Mrs Forster, and Kitty and me, except my Aunt, for we were forced to borrow one of her gowns; and you cannot imagine how well he looked! When Denny, and Wickham, and Pratt, and the men came in, they did not know him in the least. Lord! How I laughed! So did Mrs Forster. I thought I should have died. And *that* made the men suspect something, and then they soon found out what was the matter. Oh, I wish you had gone with us for we had such fun!

JANE AUSTEN

From the novel

A ROOM IN THE TOWER

JANE GREY

Lady Jane Grey is a prisoner in The Tower of London, 1554. Jane is slight and small, pale and drawn; she is talking to her waiting-woman, Mrs Tylney

(*Off*) Tylney! Is it time, Tylney?

Jane enters

I can't sleep. It's so cold in there. I have tried, but it's useless . . . useless. I haven't slept for . . . it seems years; and whenever I sleep I dream. I dream they are killing Guildford. I stand at the window and watch. It's horrible because I'm not with him. . . . I can't move! (*Jane stands by the window*) He looks up to me standing here, and when he sees me, he tries to smile so bravely. Then he takes off his ruff, and kneels down. . . . Last night I dreamt I saw my father's head on a pike. It was lifted up and waved at me through that dreadful window. His mouth was open and the blood streamed down the staff. Why have they put me into this room? When they erected the scaffold the last time, the carpenters' hammer hit the nails into my brain. It was maddening, unceasing . . . knock . . . knock . . . knock . . . knock. . . . Is there any hope, Tylney? What is there to do here except remember the past. We have such a quiet garden at home. Lavender hedges and rosemary. Arbours loaded with red and yellow roses. I used to pick the tight, sweet-smelling buds and put them in my hair. There's a little pool I sat beside to watch my goldfish, they were so pretty . . . they used to nibble the crumbs from my finger-tips. I remember stealing there on warm evenings to listen to the nightingale. There are no nightingales here, no singing birds . . . only the croak of the raven, and they forbode evil! They will come for me soon. Their footsteps will echo on those stairs . . . then someone will open the door and ask me if I am ready. (*Her hands creep to her throat*) "I am quite ready, my Lords." They will lead me down . . . round . . . and round . . . and round the staircase . . . out into the air, and the light . . . everybody will gaze at me, perhaps some of them will feel a little sorry. Where is my husband? Why can't I see him again? I only want to touch him . . . to feel his arms round me, to be sure, to be sure that he wanted me. I must beg her, implore her to let me see him. Perhaps she will understand, and have compassion on us. O God, if she spares us . . . we may be free tomorrow, in a few hours! Guildford and I . . . we will go away into the country and forget, and begin life again, together. I think he loves me enough for that. Oh, Tylney, I don't understand. How strange a place the world is. I, who have never purposely hurt anyone in my life! (*A silence*) Listen! . . . Listen! Did you hear? I thought I heard footsteps. Someone is coming. Please, stay with me. Don't leave me alone.

HUGH STEWART

46

THE BARRETS OF WIMPOLE STREET
BELLA

Cousin Bella Hedley has had her uncle's (Edward Moulton Barret) permission to have his daughter Henrietta as a bridesmaid at her forthcoming wedding. Bella with Henrietta—dressed in her bridesmaid's array—enters Elizabeth's bedroom (the invalid sister and poetess.) Their other sister, Arabel, is in the room

(*Bella is an exquisitely pretty, exquisitely turned-out little creature, voluble, affected, sentimental, with a constitutional inability to pronounce her r's*) I think Uncle Edward is most fwightfully thwilling! I adore that stern and gloomy type of gentleman. It's so exciting to coax and manage them. And so easy—if you know how! And I weally think I do. . . . But what I can't understand is his extwaordinawy attitude towards love and ma'wiage, and all that. It isn't as if he were in any way a mis—mis—oh, what's the howwid word? Ah, yes, a misogynist. He isn't. Never mind how I know, but I *do* know. . . . Besides, didn't he mawwy himself—and, what's more, have eleven childwen? . . . (*An uncomfortable silence*) Oh, have I said anything—vewy dweadful? I'm so sowwy! I didn't mean to be i'wevewent. . . . But I *do* find dear Uncle Edward's attitude extwaordinawy—and so useless! For in spite of it—and wight under his nose—and all unknown to him—his whole house is litewally seething with womance. (*Enthusiastically*) I think Captain Surtees Cook is quite fwightfully thwilling! The way he looks at you, dear—and looks—and looks—and looks! . . . If he ever looked at me like that my knees would twemble so that I shouldn't be able to stand, and I'd get the loveliest shivers down my back! And then, there's George! *You* may not believe it, but *I'm* absolutely certain he has a thwilling understanding with your little cousin, Lizzie. . . . And you weally mean to tell me that Charles and Miss what's-her-name are just mere fwiends? As for poor Occy—well, I don't mind telling you, in confidence, that my dear, dear Ha'wy is fwightfully jealous of him. Oh, I'm a fwightfully observant little thing! F'winstance, though you hardly ever mention his name, I know that Mr Wobert Bwowning comes here to see you at least once evewy week. And at other times he sends you flowers. And he often bwings little cakes for dear Flush! . . . Flush! . . . Oh, wouldn't it be fwightfully intewesting if only dear Flush could speak! (*To Arabel*) You see, dear Flush is the only witness of all that goes on at Ba's weekly *tête-à-tête* with the handsomest poet in England. He—Flush, I mean—ought to know a wonderful lot about poetwy by this time! For when two poets are gathered together they talk about whymes and whythms all the time? Or don't they? . . . I'm fwightfully ignowant. But of course, I won't breathe a word of it to Uncle Edward. I'm all on the side of womance, and the path of twue love, and all that.

RUDOLF BESIER

THE FLIES

ELECTRA

Agamemnon was murdered by his wife Clytemnestra and her lover Aegistheus (who is now the new King). Every year a Festival of Death is celebrated, and flies plague the people. Agamemnon's daughter Electra, who is no better than a servant in the palace, is waiting for the time when a certain young man will come to avenge her father's death. The young man is her brother Orestes

(*A public square in Argos dominated by a statue of Zeus, god of flies and death. Electra comes forward, carrying a large bin. She goes up to the statue of Zeus, without seeing Orestes and the Tutor*) Yes, you old swine, scowl away at me with your goggle eyes and your fat face all smeared with raspberry juice—scowl away, but you won't scare me, not you! They've been to worship you, haven't they, those pious matrons in black dresses. They've been padding round you in their big creaky shoes. And you were pleased, old bugaboo, it warmed your silly wooden heart. You like them old, of course; the nearer they are to corpses, the more you love them. They've poured their choicest wines out at your feet, because it's your festival today, and the stale smell from their petticoats tickled your nostrils. (*She rubs herself against him*) Now smell me for a change, smell the perfume of a fresh, clean body. But of course I'm young, I'm alive—and you loathe youth and life. I, too, am bringing you offerings, while all the others are at prayers. Here they are: ashes from the hearth, peelings, scraps of offal crawling with maggots, a chunk of bread too filthy even for our pigs. But your darling flies will love it, won't they, Zeus? A good feast-day to you, old idol, and let's hope it is your last. I'm not strong enough to pull you down. All I can do is to spit at you. But some day he will come, the man I'm waiting for, carrying a long, keen sword. He'll look you up and down, and chuckle, with his hands on his hips, like this, and his head thrown back. Then he'll draw his sword and chop you in two, from top to bottom—like this! So the two halves of Zeus will fall apart, one to the left, one to the right, and everyone will see he's made of common wood. Just a lump of cheap white deal, the terrible God of Death! And all that frightfulness, the blood on his face, his dark green eyes and all the rest—they'll see it was only a coat of paint. You, anyhow, you know, you're white inside, white as a child's body, and you know, too, that a sword can rip you limb from limb, and you won't even bleed. Just a log of deal—anyhow it will serve to light our fires next winter. (*She notices Orestes*) Oh, I say! You won't tell on me, will you? I'm only a servant here. The least of the servants in the Palace. I wash the King's and Queen's underlinen. And how dirty it is, all covered with spots and stains! Yes, I have to wash everything

48

they wear next to their skin, the shifts they wrap their rotting bodies in, the nightdresses Clytemnestra has on when the King shares her bed. I shut my eyes and scrub with all my might. I have to wash up, too. You don't believe me? See my hands, all chapped and rough. Why are you looking at them in that funny way? Do they, by any chance, look like the hands of a princess? Every morning I've to empty the dustbin. I drag it out of the palace, and then—well, you saw what I do with the refuse. That big fellow in wood is Zeus. God of Death and Flies. The other day, when the High Priest came here to make his usual bows and scrapings, he found himself treading on cabbage-stumps and rotten turnips and mussel-shells. He looked startled, I can tell you! I say! You won't tell on me, will you?

JEAN-PAUL SARTRE

ENTER A FREE MAN

LINDA

George Riley lives in a dream-world—he is free. Free from the responsibility of a job, free from providing for his family, and free from National Assistance, as he is employed as an inventor. Linda, his long-suffering, pocket-money-providing daughter, gets fed up with the whole farce of it, and speaks her mind to her mother

Try to be charitable! Try? I am a charity, I work at it full-time. You and me, we're the Society for the Preservation of George Riley! God, if his father hadn't died, he wouldn't even have a house to live in! (*Calls upstairs*) Dad! Well, I hope he's calmed down since yesterday. I don't like waiting for the balloon to pop in his face. It's bad for my nerves. I'm not unkind. I mean I don't feel unkind. Funny thing is I'm more embarrassed than he is when he comes back from his little outings. I never know what to say, and it's *weird* pretending it never happened. (*Calls again*) Dad! Wash your hands! If he was honest he'd come down and say, "I've decided that some people are cut out to make a living and some people are cut out to lie in bed, and I'm the bed type so I'll be upstairs if you want me and if you're not doing anything at four o'clock I'll have a cup of tea . . . two lumps." Instead of that, he sits up there doing damn all. It's a situation, isn't it? You can't expect me to be sentimental about him. I mean, life hasn't been like a National Savings advert, has it? All the happy family round the fire and the ruddy spaniel chewing the slipper. (*Pause*) Anyway, I don't mean he's mad or anything. If he was Lord Riley he'd be called eccentric. But he's just plain old George. So he's half-barmy. How can he go on like that? Ever since I remember he's been going up to that damn room. What does he do it for? Why doesn't he just sit downstairs and stop pretending? It used to be so nice . . . once . . . at that crummy school . . . "What does your dad do? . . . *My* dad's an inventor. Most of their dads were just bus conductors and milkmen and labourers and mechanics. Some of them didn't have jobs at all. But my dad was an inventor! . . . Amazing how long it took me to see through that! I must have been thick. So what am I supposed to do now, join in the game? Well, I don't think I'm going to play much longer. I'm not enjoying it.

TOM STOPPARD

EASY MONEY

JACKY

The Stafford family find that they have won a large football dividend, and although some easy money would be welcome, their plans of how to spend the fortune evoke quarrels. Jacqueline Worrell, their niece, confesses that she has forgotten to post the coupon. The next day Jacky is found sitting gloomily by the fire, when Martha, the elderly maid servant, enters

(*Starting*) Who's that? Oh, it's you, Martha! People are funny. Yesterday morning, when it all happened, I thought it was just the right moment. Aunt Ruth said she wished they'd never won the pool, and Uncle Philip said he wished it, and Carol said she wished it, too! I thought they'd be glad when I told them. But they weren't! I didn't expect Dennis to be glad because he had some scheme on and wanted the money. But the others. . . . Grandma, the venomous, old witch! That's the one really good thing— she's gone! It was terrible here yesterday afternoon and evening—the atmosphere. Dennis went straight out and didn't come back till midnight. Carol sat in her room, crying. Grandma was upstairs, packing, and Uncle Philip and Aunt Ruth wouldn't speak to one another. It was awful. I've done something else wrong, too. I've stolen something. Yes, I have—my school report. It came by the second post. I recognized the envelope. Miss Eames always sends it to Uncle Philip and he reads it and forwards it to Nairobi. I didn't feel very CONFIDENT about it, so I opened it. It said "Conduct—fair. Lacks concentration and perseverance. Could do much better if she applied herself to the task at hand. Apt to be forgetful and careless." Forgetful and careless! That's a nice thing to have said about me at a time like this, isn't it? I tore it up and burnt it! Fancy sending out school reports a week before Christmas—even the Nazis didn't do things like that! So I've decided NOT to be honest in the future. In fact I think I've decided to live an immoral life. I wish I'd started yesterday and not told them about the football pool.

Later in the scene Jacky talks to her Uncle Philip

Uncle Philip? You said you were going to ring Miss Eames about my report. There's no need. It's come! My report. It's rather difficult to explain. (*She hesitates*) It was like this. It came with a lot of other letters, and I'm afraid I opened it—accidentally. Then—I was reading it and I dropped it and it fell into the fire and was burnt. Unfortunate, wasn't it? I don't remember all the details. It said "Conduct—excellent. A great improvement all round." Yes, won't father be pleased. (*She goes to the door, then turns*) Uncle Philip! Would you like to know what it REALLY said? It said "Conduct very bad indeed. This girl is a liar, a cheat and a complete louse." (*She runs to him and kneels at his feet*) Oh, Uncle Philip,

51

I'm so sorry! I don't think I'm very good at villainy. I should have felt awful if you'd believed me. D'you know, Uncle Philip, you're rather a deceptive character—you're not half so innocent as you seem. They won't be very pleased with that report in Nairobi. (*She hesitates*) I don't suppose you could . . . (*She stops*) You're an awfully decent type, Uncle Philip. I often wonder why you have such a forgiving nature.

ARNOLD RIDLEY

A LAST BELCH FOR THE GREAT AUK

DYMPHNE PUGH-GOOCH

Dymphne Pugh-Gooch's flat has been let, without her knowledge, to a Northern Ornithologist—Reg Armitage. The scenes are enacted in a multi-viewpoint manner—how the two characters see themselves and as they see each other. In this extract Dymphne is explaining to Armitage what it is like to be a photographic model

I have to get up at seven-thirty, yes seven-thirty, and make myself a breakfast which is nourishing but not fattening. You don't have to worry, you can eat what you like. But I have to watch my diet the whole time. I can't have a day off, not because it's a fad but because it's an essential part of my job to remain slim. When I dine out I have to count the calories of each dish. I have to remain slim but at the same time I must have bags of energy. That's why I have to have a good balanced breakfast. I shan't get a break until about two o'clock and I can't allow myself any snacks between meals. This is all part of my job. After breakfast I wash, dress and make-up. Then I have to check the clothes and accessories I shall need for the day. I have to lug piles of accessories everywhere I go. A great bag full, because I must have the right selection for each job. If I turn up at a studio without the right ones bang go the chances of another booking. So I have to be very careful about checking my list. As soon as I've done it I ring for a taxi. Again, it's no luxury. I have to use taxies because I've so much to carry and I have to get from job to job at maximum speed. Into the taxi and my first stop is the hairdressers, I have to have an elaborate hair-set for the first booking of the day. I must always appear well-groomed, I must continually pay attention to my hair, clothes, nails. So I have to endure all the demands of a hair-set at nine o'clock in the morning. No sooner is it done than I'm on my way by taxi to my first booking. I check into the studio and change my make-up. The photographer sits me on a hard stool and without altering my basic position I have to turn my head from side to side, a little up, a little down, a fraction this way, a fraction that, smile, laugh, smile, frown, stare, all in an instant, whilst the photographer goes snap, snap, snap. If I don't do it there are a lot of other models who can. The lights glare, you've never felt the heat of those lamps, they burn away, the stool starts to press into my behind, my back begins to ache and then each muscle, one by one, ten minutes, twenty minutes, thirty minutes, I have to go on turning, smiling, turning, always looking fresh until after about an hour the photographer has as many shots as he wants. Back into the dressing-room, off with the make-up, brush out the hair-set and into another taxi. The next job is out of doors, my hair must look natural. I meet the photographer and we go to Hyde Park. I have to run down the steps of a monument towards the camera. As soon as

I've reached the bottom I have to go to the top again. I have to do this thirty-six times. Each time I have to look fresh, gay and alive, completely spontaneous, thirty-six times. Each one with minor variations. And that's only the first set-up. I have to change into another coat and run across the grass, then jump over a railing and then dance, each time a different costume and a different action, each time thirty-six shots or more, over and over again, through about twenty set-ups, and I must never show that I'm exhausted. But exhausted or not, no sooner is the session finished than I'm hailing another taxi. En route to the next job, as the taxi hurtles along, I have to prepare my hair for later, there'll be no other time, I have to spray and lacquer it and put it in rollers, all in the taxi as it speeds towards a couturier's for a dress fitting. At the fitting I have to stand absolutely still for half an hour at least while people pin and tack and argue all around me. By the time I'm out of the fitting it's one forty-five and I have another booking at two o'clock. Quarter of an hour for lunch. A quick sandwich in a coffee bar. I can only eat the fillings. The bread I have to leave even though I'm starving. Another taxi dash. An advertising studio. An elaborate set. A very important shot. Squeeze into the dressing-room. Crammed with boxes, clothes, accessories, other models. Squeeze to get in at all. Squeeze to get a corner of the mirror. On to the set. Stand for half an hour. The technicians check the lights, the wires, the props, check, check, check. I mustn't move. Into my make-up, into my dress, a very expensive evening gown, into my position for the shot. Take it again, take it again, don't move, take it again, for an hour. Off with the dress, off with the make-up, off in a taxi. Shots for a magazine. Urgently needed. Tense atmosphere. Bad tempers. Shot. Shot. Shot. Shot. At last it's over. What now? Can I go home? Put my feet up. No. Oh no. I dash home. Oh yes. I bathe, I dress. I do my hair. An important executive. Important studio. Important dinner. Bore. Bore. Bore. I have to effervesce. Until midnight. Yes midnight. When at last I arrive home. And go to bed. To get up again at seven-thirty the next morning.

DAVID HALLIWELL

The author has kindly given his permission to print this extract
(from 'A Last Belch for the Great Auk', unpublished)
Please contact: Sheila Lemon, Peter Crouch Plays Ltd,
National House, 60–6 Wardour Street, London W1V 4HA

I AM A CAMERA

SALLY BOWLES

This play is based on Christopher Isherwood's short story "Sally Bowles" from The Berlin Stories. *The action of the play takes place in a room in Fraulein Schneider's flat in Berlin in 1930. In this scene Sally, who is young and attractive, meets Christopher for the first time, being introduced by a mutual friend, Fritz Wendel*

(*Sally comes in with Fritz behind her. Shaking hands with Christopher*) I'm terribly glad to meet you. Oh, no coffee for me. I'm allergic to coffee. I come out in the most sinister spots if I drink it before dinner. I always have prairie oysters for breakfast. Don't you adore them? Eggs with Worcester sauce all sort of wooshed up together. I simply live on them. (*Sits, draping cloak over head of couch*) Actually, I suppose I couldn't have a whisky and soda, could I? I'm simply dead. Do you have anything? I mean, anything besides coffee? Dear old mother's ruin. Gin will be wonderful. Am I terribly late, Fritz darling? I thought I wasn't going to be able to come at all. I had a most frantic row with my landlady. Finally, I just said "Pig!" and swept out. I'll just have it straight. In a tooth glass? That will be wonderful. Give me one of your marvellous cigarettes, Fritz darling. (*Fritz offers cigarettes*) Do you ever smoke any of Fritz's cigarettes? (*Takes holder from her handbag, fits cigarette into it and lights it*) They're absolutely devastating. I'm sure they're full of opium, or something. They always make me feel terribly sensual. Thank you so much. This looks wonderful. (*Sips it*) Oh, it is. It's got an extraordinary taste, like peppermint. I think it is wonderful. Have some, Fritz. (*Hands Fritz the glass*) Taste it. Perhaps we can all make a fortune selling mint-flavoured gin. (*Handing glass to Christopher*) You have some, too. Oh, the row was absolutely awful. You should have heard the things she called me. I mean— well, I suppose in a way I may be a bit of a tart. . . . I mean, in a nice way—but one doesn't like to be called that. Just because I brought a man home with me last night. And, anyway, I'm terribly in love with him. You'll never guess. Klaus. Yes. He was always just like part of the piano to me. And then last night he was absolutely astonishing. Just like a faun, or something. He made me feel like a most marvellous nymph, miles away from anywhere, in the middle of the forest. And then the land-lady came in and made the most boring remarks, so I simply can't go back. (*Finishes drink and hands glass to Fritz*) I shall have to find a new room. (*To Christopher*) I don't suppose you know of any, do you? Some-thing like this, perhaps? Is it terribly expensive? Fifty? But that's nothing. I pay eighty for mine. This is very nice. (*Looks around*) Is that your bed? Oh, I think that's sweet—all hidden away like that. (*Looks behind the curtains*) Oh, that's where you keep things. You mean I could really have

55

this? How soon? (*Coming down to Christopher*) What is Fraulein Schneider like? I mean, is she going to make trouble if I bring men home occasionally? I mean, it would only be very occasionally, because I do think one ought to go to the man's rooms, if one can. I mean, it doesn't look so much as if one was sort of expecting it. (*Kneels on couch*) And men feel very keenly about that sort of thing. And it won't be men, anyway. It'll only be Klaus. I've decided to be absolutely faithful to him. I really have. She wouldn't mind that, would she, or would she? I say, am I shocking you, talking like this?

JOHN VAN DRUTEN

Adapted from the stories by Christopher Isherwood

Published by Evans Brothers Ltd

THE DAY AFTER THE FAIR

ANNA

The play is set in a West-Country cathedral town. Edith Harnham, the wife of a wealthy brewer, takes a personal interest in one of her maids—Anna, an uneducated eighteen-year-old village girl. One day, whilst at the fair, Anna met Charles Bradford. On returning to London, Charles corresponded with her, but Anna, a semi-illiterate, asked her mistress, Edith, to reply to the letters for her. In this scene Anna has just returned from a visit to the village

My brother-in-law's just off home, Ma'am, and he said I was to thank you for his supper which he much enjoyed. (*With a glance at Arthur Harnham*) Shall I come back when it's more convenient, Ma'am? Only you did say that as soon as . . . (*Anna breaks off as Arthur, irritated by the interruption, strides towards his study*) Oh, Ma'am! Everything looks so small in the village. I don't ever want to go back there now. I doubt I'd have had that much of a welcome if you hadn't given me that lovely basket of good things to take, Ma'am. I don't mean that not in any nasty way, Ma'am. It's just that there's not a mouthful to spare. Fifteen shillings a week he gets, and four children to keep. Rose is my only close relation now, Ma'am, but she's not the kind I could ever turn to for anything. Life's ever so hard for them. Oh, I had to tell them about Charles, Ma'am, I couldn't hold it back —not with Wednesday so close now. Besides, all through the day I'm saying to myself, this time on Wednesday he'll be on the train. And then, this time on Wednesday I'll be at the station waiting for him—and then, this time on Wednesday we'll both be together again. So I had to speak about him, Ma'am. Another letter? But—in the last letter he said he wouldn't write again, Ma'am, because he'd be here so soon. (*Edith holds out the letter to Anna*) Would you read it out for me please, Ma'am. (*Taking the envelope reluctantly*) Very well, Ma'am. (*She takes the letter from its envelope and begins to read*) "Dearest, I am quite . . ." (*She pauses, puzzled by a word*) D-e-s-p-o- . . . (*Saying the word after Edith*) Despondent. But why, Ma'am. Why should he? (*Reading slowly*) "It is with a heevy . . ." "It is with a heavy heart that I find myself obliged to send you the dismal . . ." (*Pause*) I-n-f-o-r-m- . . . (*Edith takes the letter and begins to read briskly*) Does it mean he's not coming, Ma'am? Oh, but I . . . (*Faintly*) Next month? Oh, Ma'am! (*Her knees give way and she sinks to the floor in a faint*) (*Edith fetches the smelling salts and holds them to Anna's nose*) Oh, Ma'am. What? . . . No, Ma'am, no. I—I don't need to see a doctor, Ma'am. It's not a doctor I *need*, Ma'am, it's Charles. You won't turn me out, Ma'am, will you? Please—please say you won't turn me out. Only I can't keep it to myself, not for another whole month, can I? I've had all the signs, Ma'am. And Rose, she knows all about *them*. If you was to turn me out now, Ma'am, whatever would become of me? But when Charles finds out what's happened to me, he'll stand by me—won't he, Ma'am? He loves me. He's always saying he loves me. Oh, I want to tell him now, Ma'am. I couldn't wait for another whole month not knowing what his feelings are, could I? Oh, Ma'am, please write and say he's to come down at once, so we can make our arrangements and settle things, and that way I'll have peace of mind. When you come to the end of the letter, will you say I love him still very much—please?

FRANK HARVEY

Based on the short story "On the Western Circuit"
by THOMAS HARDY

THE GOOD PERSON OF SZECHWAN

SHEN TEH

Shen Teh, a prostitute, lodges the Gods for a night who come to Earth to find a good person. They give her some money with which she purchases a tobacconist's shop; but she finds that she cannot remain good and survive. So she disguises herself as her male cousin—Shui Ta. In this trial scene Shui Ta is accused of murdering Shen Teh, and the Gods are the judges

(*Shui Ta has collapsed on to his chair*) I can't go on. If the court can be cleared so that only the magistrates are present I will make a confession. Have they gone? All of them? I cannot hold out any longer. Illustrious Ones, I have recognized you! Let me confess the frightful truth. I am your good person! (*He takes off his mask and rips away his costume. Shen Teh stands there*)

Yes, it is me, Shui Ta and Shen Teh, I am both of them.
 Your original order
To be good while yet surviving
Split me like lightning into two people I
Cannot tell what occurred: goodness to others
And to myself could not both be achieved.
To serve both self and others I found too hard.
Oh, your world is arduous! Such need, such desperation!
The hand which is held out to the starving
Is quickly wrenched off! He who gives help to the lost
Is lost for his own part! For who could
Hold himself back from anger when the hungry are dying?
Where could I find so much that was needed, if not
In myself? But that was my downfall! The load of commandments
Forced me into the sludge. Yet if I broke the rules
I strode proudly around, and could eat myself full!
Something is wrong with this world of yours. Why
Is wickedness so rewarded, and why is so much suffering
Reserved for the good? Oh, I felt such
Temptation to treat myself kindly! I felt too
A secret awareness inside me, for my foster-mother
Washed me with slops from the gutter! So I acquired
A sharp eye. And yet pity
Brought me such pain that I at once felt wolfish anger
At the sight of misery. Then
I could feel how I gradually altered and
My lips grew tight and hard. Bitter as ashes
The kind word felt in my mouth. And yet
I should gladly have been an Angel to the slums. For giving

59

Was still my delight. A smiling face
And I walked in the clouds.
Condemn me: each of my crimes
Was committed to help out my neighbour
To love my beloved or
To save my young son from going without.
O Gods, for your vast projects
I, poor human, was too small.

*At a sign from the First God the ceiling opens. A pink cloud descends. On it
the three Gods mount slowly upwards*

Oh no, Illustrious Ones! Do not go away! Don't leave me! How am I to
face the two good old people who lost their shop, or the water-seller
with his stiff hand? And how can I protect myself against the barber,
whom I don't love, and how against Sun, whom I do? And my body has
been blessed; soon my little son will be there and wanting to eat. I cannot
remain here. (*She looks frantically towards the door through which her
tormentors will come*) Oh, do not go away, Illustrious Ones! I haven't told
you all! I need you terribly! Help!

Shen Teh stretches desperately towards them as they disappear upwards

BERTOLT BRECHT

Translated by John Willett